In Search of Mermaids

In Search of
Mermaids

THE MANATEES OF GUIANA

~~~~~~~~~~

Colin Bertram

THOMAS Y. CROWELL COMPANY
New York   *Established 1834*

First published in the United States of America in 1964

Copyright © 1963 by Colin Bertram

Printed in the United States of America

Library of Congress Catalog Card No. 64–20091

1   2   3   4   5   6   7   8   9   10

1261328

For Arthur Goodland,
the perfect host in
Georgetown, B.G.

Contents

Introduction

THIS BOOK is written in the hope that it will help the conservation of the manatees of the Guianas, of British Guiana in particular. They are in need, first, of more adequate protection against foolish killing for fun and, then secondly, of conservative practices so that they may prove of some long-term usefulness to the people of their homeland. Manatees have been more in the public eye recently than ever before because of a suggestion that they might prove useful in the control of excessive growth of weeds in newly-formed, man-made African lakes. The theoretical possibilities and the practical improbabilities of this interesting suggestion are here included.

Others have set out [1] the folklore of 'mermaids' and the possible connection with manatees. This topic is not here pursued, but it is possible that manatees and the related dugongs, more than any other particular species, may have seemed to corroborate earlier flights of fancy.

The manatees of the Guianas, because of the very nature of the beasts, are extremely difficult to observe and study, more particularly now that they are less abundant than previously,

[1] For example *Sea Enchantress: the Tale of the Mermaid and her Kin*, by Given Benwell and Arthur Waugh. Hutchinson. 1961.

and no longer appear on the public market in numbers convenient for biological observation and dissection.

An attempt is made in this book to create more public interest in manatees and to promote a knowledge and appreciation of the Sirenians, just as there exists already a very widespread interest in, for example, seals and whales. Widespread public interest, even at a distance, is at least the beginning of a form of protection for species in need of it.

The mermaids or manatees are first described in their Guianan setting and then the prospects seemingly before the manatees are described. Yet the general fascination to the biologist of tropical South America cannot be excluded; and, whatever one writes, that fascination, in scenes and species, comes bubbling forth. Later there is description of the other Sirenians or Seacows which exist elsewhere in the world—the widespread dugong now becoming rare and Steller's Seacow which was exterminated within so few years of its discovery.

Since, too, whatever conservation of manatees may be brought about must be maintained in the Guianas, some picture is provided of the background scene[1] in that region of biological delight, historical interest, and human volatility. Courteous kindly people of diverse origins make the path of the visitor so very pleasant, and every newcomer must surely be most grateful for the numerous kindnesses received from people in many walks of life.

My wife and I made our study of the manatees of the Guianas early in 1962, primarily in B.G. but with visits to Surinam and briefly to Cayenne. We were close witnesses of

1 For details of B.G.'s history, economy and social structure see Raymond T. Smith's *British Guiana*, issued under the auspices of the Royal Institute of International Affairs. Oxford University Press. 1962.

those most regrettable riots and fires in Georgetown on
'Black Friday' 16 February.[1] Those riots and racial tensions
will have perhaps served a useful purpose if their fundamental
human and biological cause can be sufficiently appreciated
and, now, avoiding action deliberately initiated.

My wife, Dr C. K. Ricardo Bertram, had previously worked
extensively on the freshwater fisheries of Central Africa and
of the Middle East, thus complementing my own previous
work on marine mammals. We only regretted that our period
in the Guianas—a sabbatical term from Cambridge and a
family—could not be extended.

We express our most sincere thanks to those bodies and
institutions which made our activities possible financially.
They were, jointly, the New York Zoological Society, the
Nuffield Foundation, the Zoological Society of London, The
Foreign Travel Fund of the University of Cambridge, and the
Eugenics Society.

1 See REPORT of a Commission of Inquiry into Disturbances
in British Guiana in February 1962. London. H.M.S.O. Colonial
No. 354. 1962.

In Search of Mermaids

1

~~~~~~~~~~~

Mermaids in the Mud

THE MERMAID and her mate at first sight have little to
endear them. The grey skin is constantly sloughing; the broad
tail is usually chipped at its edge, while the back is often green
with algal filaments and slime. The body is set with single
hairs scattered an inch apart while the muzzle has bristles
aplenty, increasing to become stiff papillae within the lips.
The fore limbs or flippers are short and tipped by three rough
nails. The length may be eight or nine or perhaps even twelve
feet long.

The eyes are round and small and close more nearly with
a sphincter than with lids—no ogling maiden there. Truly the
body is plump but the neck is neither slim nor evident, the
body and shoulders sloping gradually to the head. There are
no hind limbs to excite the attention of the wandering sailor's
eye, so that one must conclude that it was the breasts alone
which stimulated thoughts of sea maidens and delight. The
breasts indeed are a single pair and pectoral, as in man,
monkeys, and bats. So are they pectoral in the elephant where
the positioning is much as in the manatee—close in to the base
of the forelimb. In the manatee the teat seems almost to be on
the actual hinder edge of the thick flipper, just where it joins
the body. When lactating maybe the gland is large and

shapely, but it must have been sailors very far from home and girl companionship who could truly think the manatee a sea maiden delightful to the eye.

Yet watching manatees daily, with the eye of the zoologist and a capability of wide comparison, there is a something which makes these animals fascinating and curiously attractive, though certainly not endearing nor seductive. There is the quiet torpedo motion through the water, impelled by the imperceptible movement of that broad, oval tail. There is the occasional backward motion by a curling downward of the tail. There is the quietness of the breathing, not a sound as the nostrils reach the surface, open, and withdraw in two seconds without commotion, without even a ripple. But most of all there is the wrinkling of the rubbery snout as it searches the floating surface vegetation and begins to mandibulate its entry to the mouth; or when, as occasionally it does in the quietness of dawn, it draws its head and shoulders laboriously from the water by the effort of its flippered forelimbs pressing the ground with their nailed tips, so as to feed on succulent bankside vegetation. Then one has for the manatee the kind of admiration which one showers in one's heart upon a clever cripple—perhaps one who paints with the brush held between his toes or, handless, plays a xylophone.

Oddly enough the wrinkling feeding snout has, much magnified, resemblance to the proboscis of certain bristly sea worms. The wrinkled flexibility, the rubbery texture, and the surprising flat terminal disc, all enhance that resemblance which to a zoologist will be familiar. More surprising still, and again with much resemblance to these Polychaete worms, the manatee has what we may aptly term pseudo-mandibles. Its mouth is not just ox-like and horizontal with a prehensile tongue, nor is it a tooth-armed slit beneath a tough nasal disc as in a pig. There are no incisors, no front teeth, nothing but changing molar teeth set far back in the jaws. The special feature of the manatee's mouth is that its two corners themselves function as active projecting mandibles, like the sea worm's mandibles, pressing in the food with regular pincer movements. This is very curious indeed. The corners of the mouth can be projected and then opposed to one another, dragging in the vegetation with their tough papillae-covered points. These opposing 'mandibles', these oddly active corners of the mouth, in use are pink or yellowish, a part of the normal inside of the mouth, having not the grey colouration of the muzzle and the remainder of the manatee's rough skin. Photographs show well this curious use and conformation whose description is so difficult and whose action perhaps is hard to visualize. The forelimbs too are used actively to sweep and press vegetation towards and into the mouth.

To the zoologist, so curious a feature has a special fascination, and that is near akin to endearment. That is very far removed from whatever, and almost unbelievable, fascination the female manatee may once have had for hungry seamen far from home and female friends. Many species of seal must surely have had for simple seamen a far greater elegance, attractiveness of eye, docility of mien and snug furriness than the grey and rough-skinned bristly-nosed manatee.

By tradition, too, mermaids are—or were—creatures of the sea, usually on rocky places and in sunshine. Such features are certainly more seal-like than Sirenian—if we use the zoological adjective descriptive of the group to which belong the Seacows, both manatee and dugong. Further, no one ever seemed interested in the diet of traditional mermaids but, since they have for centuries been depicted with teeth of very human form, presumably it has been supposed that they were as ourselves omnivorous, with a strong tendency towards a

more fleshy diet as wealth becomes available. No one seems to
have hinted that the mermaids lacked front teeth and were
totally confined to a steady diet of varied aquatic vegetation.

Modern Guianese mermaids, manatees, are more un-
traditional still, for they not only lack charm, front teeth and
long tresses of glamorous hair, but they live almost invariably
in muddy places. This last they can scarcely avoid doing for,
being dependent upon aquatic vegetation for their food, they
must seek it where it grows—and that is mostly in muddy,
silty places and not where the water is clear. Additionally,
apart from the black-water forest creeks where the water is
clear if dark, almost all water on the north coast of South
America is turbid—coastal, estuarine and riverine alike. The
enormous rivers of the region carry seawards huge loads of
fine silt and mud so that all coastal waters are shallow, thick,
brown and soup-like, and indeed not very saline either, so
great is the admixture of water from the land. Likewise the
enormous rivers themselves, tidal for tens or even hundreds of
miles inland, are turbid and filled with mud. Thus the Guianese
mermaids see much of mud, indeed they are commonly
smeared with it and have green algae growing on their slimy
backs. Yet in such places they find their food and muddy waters
are certainly conducive to that invisibility which they seem to
seek. This is no denial that manatees live, too, in clearer waters
far upstream in certain rivers, savanna regions; but indubitably the mermaids of the Guianas are mostly in the
mud.

The special feature of tradition was of course that, by repute,
the mermaid, manatee or Seacow, could suckle her young one
when positioned vertically in the water. The mother's whole
head and neck would be out of the water, as would be the head
of the sucker held by the mother's forelimb, incurved across her
chest. This picture of maternal solicitude and suckling sounds

quite probable, but there seems to be no reputable record of the occurrence ever having been observed in modern times. Indeed the evidence is contrary. The modern manatee—at any rate the Florida manatee which has been much the most observed in detail[1]—suckles under water with mother and calf in the same plane horizontally and at a convenient angle to one another. On the other hand the Indo-Pacific mermaids, the dugongs, possibly have different habits though they are certainly not properly recorded. I was once assured, in the Gulf of Aqaba by Arab seamen, that the dugong, there an extremely rare animal, had by them been seen to suckle in the vertical and 'traditional' style. The dugong is of course a much more truly marine mammal than is the estuarine and river manatee.

In comparison, the pelvic-teated whales suckle in mid-ocean with the whole young one submerged like its mother, with the occasional exception of the blow-hole on the top of the head. The seals, on the other hand, only suckle on land, dog-like, the mother lying suitably on her side and presenting her single pair of teats to the pup. Such interesting information as the composition of manatee milk is quite unknown as yet. It may be supposed that it is a much less powerful fluid than, for example, the milk of the Elephant Seal which had nearly 50 per cent of fat, enabling the young one to grow from 100 lb at birth to four times that weight in 22 days, so to acquire a thick covering of blubber. It is reasonable to expect that the period of suckling in the manatee is extended, considerable time elapsing before the grinding teeth are fully sufficient to allow a completely independent life. But this is all surmise for the evidence has yet to be collected.

The actual birth of a mermaid calf has only been witnessed in

1 See J. C. Moore, *American Museum of Natural History*. 'Novitates'. No. 1811. 1956. 'Observations of Manatees in Aggregations'.

'seaquaria' in the United States. The salient features[1] seem to be that the calf, at three feet or so in length and weighing perhaps thirty pounds or more from an eight or nine foot cow, is born under water and is helped to the surface by its mother. The calf is then solicitously assisted for a while, even on occasion riding on the mother's back. The calf's duration of time beneath the surface, short at first, soon elongates towards the adult habit of breath-taking every few minutes. The calf for the first few hours of independent life may have the tail curled forward under the body, having been born in that position. And certainly it seems that at first the calf swims by its flippers and not by the tail alone in the adult fashion.

It is a fair, if loose, anatomical and behavioural description to stress that the Seacows are intermediate between the fully aquatic whales and dolphins, which never have connection with the land, and the seals all of whose aquatic adaptation is yet insufficient to allow them to give birth and suckle in the water. The manatees copulate, and give birth in the water, and there they suck and suckle. Certainly the manatees cannot leave the water, but indubitably they are still interested in the land. There is plenty of evidence and record that they frequently heave the forepart of the body from the water and, on a suitably sloping bank, feed on waterside vegetation. To do that they use their flippers as props, resting and heaving on their knuckles. The whole head and shoulders, perhaps indeed the foremost third of the body, may come to rest on land.

When dragged from the water, dragged ashore by men, the manatee cannot struggle back even on level ground. It cannot heave itself along, like a most ungainly looper caterpillar, as is done quickly even by that most aquatic of seals, the Weddell of Antarctica, whose foreflippers are not used at all in progression

1 ibid. Also J. C. Moore, *Journal of Mammalogy*, Vol. 38, No. 1 1957. 'Newborn young of a captive manatee'.

on the land or over ice. The manatee is bound by gravity and cannot regain its aquatic environment unless on at least a gentle slope towards the water and headed in the right direction. Yet there is a tale of one heaving itself from one side to the other of a barrier in a narrow channel, a barrier a foot above the surface and a foot or two across. That was in the Botanic Gardens in Georgetown: the feat sounds not improbable, more particularly if spurred by hunger.

The mermaid's diet is of course entirely vegetarian, though it is not to be doubted that a good many small molluscs and other creatures are chewed with the weeds in which they hide. Catholicity of taste is evident; any weed that is soft seems to be acceptable, whether growing at the bottom, on the surface, or on the bank. In zoos cooked carrots and potatoes are reportedly acceptable. But the total bulk of vegetable matter consumed in the wild must certainly be very large, though quite inadequately measured. In the Guianas, commonly consumed plants are water lettuce, shrimp grass, fairy grass and other species with attractive names.[1]

Surreptitious is perhaps not the first but is none the less a suitable adjective to apply to Sirenians, not only for the alliterative euphony but for its truth. To be surreptitious, perhaps you need not be intelligent, though despite first appearances, intelligence is something which one attributes to the manatee after considerable observation. The small eye and ovoid head, the sluggish habit and the seeming slothfulness, leave one gradually with an appreciation that here is an animal which has found in life a happy niche which it can maintain moderately well in the face of increasing disturbance. It can do that by being intelligently surreptitious, watching, smelling, listening, all with scarcely perceptible movement.

[1] For example such plants as: *Cabomba, Anarcharis, Leersia, Utricularia, Nymphaea, Nelumbo, Eichornia*, etc. etc.

Manatees are certainly acute in their sense of hearing. This is the more remarkable if you have ever examined the head of a mermaid and failed to find her ears. No shell-like pinkness, no little brown lobes bedecked with golden danglings, just a rough grey skin, continuously sloughing its epidermis. But if you examine sufficiently closely you will find a tiny hole or little slit into which you can insert the point of a seeker, that useful tool of the zoological dissector. That is all the manatee can show for an ear.

However, invisible exteriorly as they may be, the ears of manatees are acute in the actual process of hearing. We watched on many occasions captive manatees in a trench. Once they had settled down they provided a regularity of behaviour which was instructive. In the heat of the afternoon it was their custom to be at the surface, lying in an arc with the back exposed but head and tail depressed beneath the murky water. Testing them deliberately, their actions were regular and became predictable. Undisturbed, the tip of the nostrils would be raised above the surface for air about every minute and a half. The raising of the nose for the purpose was entirely silent, and no ripple whatever was produced at the surface. Usually the top of the head and the eyes remained beneath so that the nose appeared suddenly and silently as two sixpence-sized black openings about two feet in front of the motionless arched hummock of the back. The actual exchange of air must be very small in volume as a two- or three-second surfacing produced no ripple, no sound and no indication whatever as to whether air was being expelled or inhaled. Sometimes the head was very slightly twisted so that one nostril alone would surface, open, shut and disappear, the other remaining the while invisible and shut beneath the surface.

Yet all the while the manatee is acutely listening, as can be tested. A gentle human whistle, perhaps bird-like in quality, produces no reaction. Nor is there reaction to an adjustable dog whistle—blow low, blow high, or even above the range of human ears. Nor is there reaction to a clicking with the human tongue such as is sometimes used to urge a horse from walk to trot. All these, one may fancy, have avian counterparts. A jumping on the bank, a stamping with the feet, perhaps resembling the tread of an ox, likewise has no effect upon the placid manatee with arched back and regularly appearing nostrils. But speak with human voice, even quite quietly, and sure enough the manatee will hear, will react, and will sink, again without a ripple and without a sound, vertically downwards. There is no motion forwards or backwards or sideways but only vertically. There is no stirring of the mud suggesting that perhaps a downward vertical force is exerted by the tail under-turned beneath the body. It must be supposed that this quiet sinking from the surface and from dangerous vision is brought about by a contraction of the thorax, so slightly increasing the density of the body. Once out of sight the manatee may move in any direction, but whether it remains stationary or appears elsewhere, the next surfacing will be by the nostrils alone.

It is quite evident, both from behaviour in the wild and in confinement, that there is a capacity for extremely fine adjustments in overall density so that rising and falling in the water can be under perfect and minute control. The bones are dense, while the lungs are quite enormous in proportion. The mechanism and the skill for adjustment are both available.

Though manatees undoubtedly at times take a view of the world above the surface, sometimes lifting the head quite high near the bank, one gets the impression of them, when domesticated for years in pools where people come to visit them, that they depend chiefly on auditory stimulation. The eyes are small, seemingly sphinctered rather than lidded, set high on the head and sometimes giving the impression of a curious knowingness. When domesticated, manatees will learn to react to a human whistle and come to the edge for food tossed to them or even held in a hand convenient for their mandibulation. It may be that the manatees have a natural affection for a whistle, or it may be that uningenious human beings have never tested them with other stimulants. Yet certain it is that a food-seeking reflex may soon be built upon an oft-repeated whistle. And the whistle which attracts the tame, and the voice which alarms the wild, indubitably is heard by practically invisible ears even when those ears are well beneath the surface. It must indeed be concluded that manatees are acute both in their actual hearing, and in their judgements about what they hear. They are indeed quick to learn and, in domestication, not difficult to train to simple tricks in connection with proffered food.

Though quietness is the primary attribute of the manatee, there is no doubt of the great power of its tail and the swirl and rush of the creature when badly frightened. Make but an unkind experiment and you will see. Toss a stone on to the back of a manatee at rest, back arched, semi-slumbering in sunshine at the surface in a peaceful pool or channel, and the upheaval may be tremendous. The water is threshed and thrown high in the air and a ten-foot grey-brown torpedo speeds through the water with a well-marked wake.

The river system of the Guianas is not easy to describe, and more difficult still is it to state precisely the distribution of the manatees within those rivers. However, with the aid of certain generalizations and simplifications an attempt may be made. First consider the river system. Though small, inevitably, in comparison with the tremendous Amazon, and the Orinoco, the rivers of the region are nevertheless enormous. For example, and to give the scale, Leguan Island—just one among a cluster of low, forested islands in the mouth of the Essequibo —is itself bigger in area than Barbados which supports nearly a quarter of a million people. These rivers are huge streams of dark silt-laden water of such volume that the sea comes to be of low salinity even far from land. The whole coastal region is low, flat and barely emergent above an ocean of brown turbidity. Though the Amazon may be 3,000 miles from Peruvian source to Atlantic outflow, the Essequibo in British Guiana is no mean river with a total length of 600 miles, and innumerable tributaries. Its main mouth or estuary is fifteen miles across.

In general the rivers of the Guianas run from south to north until they reach the coast which there runs from north-west to south-east. The rivers of the north-west flow rather more from the west than the south. The largest rivers of the Guianas are the Essequibo, the Demerara, the Courantyne and the Suriname. The rivers have their origin in higher country inland and flow north across a coastal plain which is at its widest to the north-west and diminishes south-eastwards until in French Guiana it scarcely exists. The very large rivers may descend from the higher land with series of rapids, but the fall in their lower reaches is very small, and many rivers have little fall throughout their length. In consequence the rivers are some-what saline for great distances from the sea and tidal much further still.

The largest rivers cut the coast at right angles, but the smaller ones tend to flow north-westwards parallel with the coast before entering the sea. This formation has already been extensively used in Surinam (Dutch Guiana) for the con-venience of water transport. Several rivers have been joined by canals, a cut being made from the point where comes the turn

north-westwards so to join the next river to the east. Thus is
formed a transport line parallel with the coast to supplement
the main river lines which provide the channels of communication through a densely-forested area.

This whole north-east corner of South America is one of unexpected levels and connections. Despite the occurrence of
blocks of high country inland, and certain coastal ridges and
mountains in the eastern part of the Guianas, there is such lack
of contours that there are seasonal watery contacts direct with
tributaries of the Amazon and the Orinoco. There is contact in
the savanna region in the wet season, across the British Guiana-
Brazilian frontier, between the Amazonian Takatu river and
the uppermost feeders of the Rupununi, itself a tributary of the
Essequibo. There is a comparable watery connection, usable
by canoes at times, between the Orinoco system and the
Barima river in north-westernmost B.G. A little tilting of the
land in the whole of this region could have a great effect on the
direction of flow and the precise outfalls of the rivers, and such
future changes would be no more than a continuation of series
of changes in the not distant past.

Inevitably in such country the rivers provide the normal
and indeed, until the advent of aircraft, almost the only means
of communication and transport. Such is their use still today
for travel and the carriage of bauxite, timber and supplies.
Road and railway links are few and almost confined to the
coastal strip of the Guianas, no more than a few miles deep.

The coastal strip itself is much cultivated as are the river
banks. But inland of that the natural vegetation predominates
the river banks being walled by 'bush' of varying density and
ecological type. Some of the rivers flow through moist
savannas which run to the actual banks, but such conditions
are mostly some considerable distance inland from the coast.
Only the greatest rivers flow through the drier inland

savannas whether high or low, some hundreds of miles from the sea.

In these lands of forests and rivers quite expectedly the easiest places have been tamed and cultivated first. Large areas remain almost untouched, even along the coast itself, under conditions comparable with what existed everywhere so few brief centuries ago. Notable in this regard is the whole coastal region of B.G. north-westward of the Pomeroon river to the border with Venezuela. Of that region little is known indeed. It may be the home of many manatees still undisturbed by men.

For convenience of summary one may integrate actual evidence of the distribution of the manatees in the Guianas and what one supposes would be their likes and dislikes having regard to their known feeding habits. This procedure, in relation to the preceding description of the rivers, leads to three main conclusions. First of all there is no evidence at all of the Guiana manatees occurring far inland in the rivers flowing through the dry savannas, nor upstream of significant rapids. Secondly one gains the impression that the manatees are primarily the inhabitants of those stretches of rivers which are bounded by grass and floating vegetation and moist savanna. Thirdly there is evidence of manatees on occasion appearing over a much wider variety of riverine conditions, extending to the tidal waters, the saline waters, the estuaries and the sea itself between the mouths of the rivers. The numbers of such animals, their movements and their food in salty places are still equally unknown.

Nor, in the Guianas, is anything in detail known of the true nature of the manatee, whether solitary or gregarious, and whether one or other always or sometimes. In any event once a stock of any mammal has been much depleted or disturbed this point may be difficult of assessment. Certainly in B.G. we came upon no hint of aggregations of the animals at particular times and in particular places.[1] On the other hand in Florida[2] there is evidence that aggregations are common in the very different circumstances obtaining there. Particular studies have been made of aggregations of manatees in the actual city of Miami. But whether these aggregations are to be attributed to an actually gregarious nature—as in many seals—or to a general liking for a particular area where warmer[3] water is available, is not quite clear. Probably the animals are indeed fundamentally gregarious. There are comparable hints of gregariousness from the accounts of former commercial hunting in Brazil of that other species of manatee which inhabits the Amazon basin.

Now, if you were to imagine yourself a river mermaid—perhaps an improper thing to do—it is not difficult to fancy a pleasant life in one or other of the many possible available locations, so diverse in their detail. A seemingly and particularly pleasant home would be in the weedy reaches of certain moderately-sized rivers, for example up the Canje Creek. There, far above turbidity and tidal influence, where the water is clear yet dark, the river is safely deep yet conveniently sloping at the sides. There is a magnificent cover, sometimes even stretching right across the river, of floating vegetation anchored to the banks. Everlasting meals and visual protection jointly cover the water's surface. Through it the mermaid can gently raise her nostrils to the air above and the lush green

1 Arthur Goodland has recently reported that a shoal of manatee had been seen in mid-1962 in the Abary River in flood.

2 J. C. Moore, 'Novitates'. ibid. See footnote p. 5.

3 J. C. Moore, *The Quarterly Journal of the Florida Academy* *Sciences*, Vol. 14, No. 1, 1951. 'The Range of the Florida Manatee p. 3. '. . . concentrations exceeding ten individuals on very col mornings gathered in the outflow of a factory outlet where it ven warm water into the river beneath the Miami Avenue Bridge'.

vegetation may be nibbled and mandibulated eternally. The sun's heat is nicely tempered and his light filters down in pleasing greenness through the leaves and matted rootlets of floating weeds and grasses. All is quiet below except when disturbed by those infernal engines and propellors, but even their waves and wash are quickly damped to nothingness by the inertia of the floating mat. Just so is the sea's swell killed as it enters an area of concentrated pack ice. And early in the day, when the manatees may wish to thrust their heads and shoulders above the surface, to taste perhaps novel kinds of plants, then the river surface is as a bright green lawn of glistening vividness. Throughout the world the colour and the surface relief are seen to such best advantage when the sun is low. In the polar regions that pleasant convenience lasts all day long and often all night too. But in these tropic lands it is for an hour alone at dawn and dusk that the world is at its visual best. Maybe the manatees appreciate these things, or maybe not. It is foolish perhaps to ponder thus when we are ignorant even as to whether mermaids possess colour vision like ourselves, the birds, many fishes, some insects but in fact few mammals. How sad to see the sky as shades of grey, and likewise the green river carpet, and the trees and the birds, however bright. The gay Jacanas, running on long toes upon the floating mat, to us are brown and black, and there is red on their heads and yellow on their beaks. And the macaws which scream so much less senselessly than uneducated girls in punts upon the Cam, those macaws are blue and yellow, red and green, long-tailed and brilliant. Do the manatees see them only grey like their own rough skins? We just don't know and must now return from fancy to reality.

Though we never saw them ourselves, reputable people informed us that at times they had seen manatees, even in recent years, feeding off the groin at Georgetown. There, at the very mouth of the mile-wide and tidal Demerara river,[1] the quiet creatures would nibble away at tangles of vegetation brought down by the ebbing tide. Caught in an eddy, or in slack water near the groin, the manatees are seen taking their evening meal—for it is in the hour before dusk, when the heat of the day is waning, that the citizens of Georgetown promenade on the groin and the adjacent sea wall. Many eyes are on the gay and well-dressed girls; others please their ears by listening to the police band's weekly concerts—so decorous, so Victorian—then promenade and sit, some beneath a huge and aged tree whose branches spread more than forty yards across. Others watch the water, and these assert that on occasions they see mermaids at their quiet browsing, a few inches of grey-brown snout, a proboscis with nostrils, nuzzling among the weedy tangles.

These sightings we believe to be entirely genuine, for our informants were from among those few who take real interest in the Guiana fauna and flora and do their best to arouse interest in the museum, the zoo and faunal conservation. These were not people who would confuse manatees with dolphins. Of these latter there are almost always some to be seen in the river mouth, disporting themselves in the delphic manner, if that adjective is allowable. These estuarine dolphins of the Guianas are *Soltania guianensis*, a species common on this coast and reaching a length of about five feet. They are small, pointed-nosed and sportive creatures, doubtless—like other porpoises and dolphins—of high intelligence, so clever that they are very rarely caught. That of course is the reason why

1 J. C. Moore in the *Journal of Mammalogy*, Vol. 32, No. 1, 1951 gives the distribution of the Florida sub-species as being shallow salt water bays and fresh or brackish waters of sluggish coastal rivers. The variety of habitat available in Florida is less than in Guiana, for example, there are no great rivers.

more is not known about the taxonomy and biology of these small Cetaceans; they are just too swift and clever to be caught conveniently by questing scientists and commercial fishermen alike. These sportive Guianan dolphins are grey above and surprisingly pink beneath, smooth crescents of glistening rubberiness and exuberant life as they leap from the water in ephemeral arcs of surprise.

There are other dolphins too, dolphins which sadly we chanced not to see, dolphins which specialize in riverine life and run far up the world's great rivers. There are Gangetic dolphins and Irrawaddy dolphins, and almost land-locked dolphins in Chinese lakes, and there are Amazonian dolphins too. The true river dolphins are mostly small and some species are totally blind and equipped with strange strap-like teeth. Yet they seem able to feed efficiently on fish in the turbid waters despite their sightlessness. There are other, more normal estuarine dolphins which run surprisingly far up into the sweet waters of the great rivers of South America. We often were told of dolphins, of sightings in the forest rivers, in the rivers crossing the savannas, and in surprising places far from the sea. The furthest point at which we heard of river dolphins, or dolphins in a river, was in the far south-west of B.G. where the Takatu river[1] is the border with Brazil. There in the broad savannas, there 1,600 miles from the mouth of the Amazon, we heard of dolphins, pink beneath, as being not un-common members of the local fauna. One member of the notable 'Melville connection' described seeing one nine feet long, locked in a deep pool in the Takatu at a time of low water.

It is only the very ignorant who mix manatees with dolphins or fancy porpoises with the spawn of whales: people as igno-rant as the too clever scholarship candidate who in a practical

1 The Amazonian manatee *T. inunguis* also occurs in this river.

examination thought some tadpoles were the spermatozoa of a whale. Porpoises are as separate from whales as swallows from eagles, or as minnows from trout and salmon. They are similar but smaller, similar that is to say to the sperm whale, all having teeth and being actively predaceous. There are no porpoise-size creatures to demonstrate in miniature the rorquals, the great plankton-eating whales. The porpoises and dolphins are not categorically separable, except by usage among the well-informed. In general, zoologists term porpoises those species of small Cetacea which are blunt of nose, while dolphins have pointed heads, beak-like snouts, and sometimes inhabit rivers. Porpoises and dolphins innumerable there are in the oceans, of perhaps a hundred species, though not all well-defined as yet, mainly because the catching is too difficult, and the incentive not enough.

The porpoises and dolphins are admirable indeed; they are intelligent and vigorous, swift and beautiful of form. In what better terms could one commend young graduates, male and female, to employers of discernment. Like young men and women, too, they commonly combine gregariousness, seasonally or in special areas, with solitude at other times and places. So may you see them disport themselves in oceans of all latitudes, seething or solitary, thousands in half an hour or none at all for days on end. But nowhere and nohow may you see them better than in the tropics with the aid of a scarcely moving topsail schooner in a glass calm sea or near it.

Climb down below the bow, beneath the bowsprit; seat yourself upon that tense chain, the dolphin scraper; and see and feel its secondary and unplanned function. Six-foot mother and two-foot porpoise child; all grey or black or splashed with white; round-headed, long-beaked, small or up to twelve feet long. They pass along, they turn upon their sides, they sometimes scrape themselves immediately beneath. There is a visual closeness between you but an unpassable environmental barrier between the two species of warm-blooded, air-breathing, sentient beings, the dolphins and yourself.

It is only in recent years that the porpoises and dolphins have begun to appear in the zoos of the world, more especially in the United States. Their antics and their aptitudes have clearly shown them to be creatures of high mental ability, and some there are who now would rate them as the apes, next to ourselves among the mammals in the quality of their minds. Such consideration should surely make us ponder all the more the damnable cruelty of the commercial killing of the whales with explosive harpoons which so often impose an hour-long torture. Such cruelty combined with irrational exploitation makes a sorry story indeed of human failing in both sense and sensibility.

It is hard to leave this delphic digression—a tribute to elegance and vitality—without reference to those astonishing feats now performed several times daily by the porpoises in 'seaquaria'. It takes personal vision rather than words to enforce belief in the capability of a large marine mammal to jump clear from the water and neatly take a cigarette from the mouth of a man leaning out twenty feet above the surface. Words will not convince that these porpoises (*Tursiops*) can stand on their tails and not only stand but move backwards in that position across the surface of the pool to catch fish thrown to excite their curiosity and stimulate their skill.

By contrast the manatees, to whom we must return, have of course about them nothing whatever of dash or bravado, no fun nor showing off. They prefer to live their lives discreetly, silently, slowly and surreptitiously; and to all this their habits are most suitably adjusted. So often a sudden mid-stream swirl, a hundred yards ahead of the speeding river-boat, is the only hint of former presence. 'That was a manatee, that was.'

Of all the fully aquatic mammals the Seacows alone are slow-moving and vegetarian. The long-headed moose may graze—or is it browse—upon the water weeds a yard beneath the surface, walking along with its head below the water. And the hippopotamus, though certainly possessing many anatomical aquatic adaptations, in fact takes the majority of its food by grazing on the land at night. The beaver, too, works on land, cutting and dragging logs, using the water both as a mode of transport and a means of safety. All the more fully adapted aquatic mammals, the whales, dolphins and porpoises, the seals, walruses and sealions, are totally carnivorous. With that mode of life goes toughness, speed and agility, and grace, a characteristic which can scarcely with truth be attributed to manatees. Perhaps grace in any event is too anthropomorphic a concept or character to use at all : certainly it is inappropriate for animals which are seldom visible.

To see manatees at all in the wild is mostly a matter of time and diligence or of chance. Knowledge must be accumulated by talking to many whose opportunity has been extended; but when that is done a real concentration of information may be obtained. When, for example, a kindly schoolmaster asks you, in mid afternoon, to address the assembled children in a far-away riverine school, and you ask how many have had manatee for dinner in the last month, or the last year or in their lives, then a lot of information is obtained which is surely accurate on integration. This was up the Canje river at a Scottish Presbyterian village at Barakara whose church is over a hundred years old, well-loved, and filled with bats—which eluded all our efforts to catch them. These children regularly saw manatees and occasionally had them for dinner. It was clear that there were considerable numbers in that stretch of the river but that deliberate hunting of manatees for food was probably rare. When one was caught by chance in a net, or perhaps got itself into a position easily to be chopped, then the children got a special meal.

The edibility of manatees is obvious, while their palatability depends upon one's circumstances, past experience and the availability of other meats. The consensus of opinion among the earlier travellers—to judge from their written words— was indubitably that the Seacow was a welcome addition to their diet. General belief today is still that the mermaids, if not highly palatable, are none the less definitely good. Their best protection, in one sense, may well be a rise in the general standard of living so that manatee meat may lose acceptability as being poor man's food. The new affluence could lead to a desire for the world-sought steaks from land cattle. Then, the usual stupid conservatism of food habit being what it is, a new generation will soon fancy that manatee is 'fishy' and unfit for food except in near starvation. On the other hand every rise in the standard of living, or increase of purchasing power, results, in the Guianas as elsewhere, in an increase in the number of firearms. Then people will shoot with increasing foolish fire-power at everything that moves—manatees included. Fortunately for the mermaids, people with newly-acquired guns are usually impatient and rush along the rivers with noisy motors, so that again elusiveness may save them.

Indubitably in the not distant past mermaids frequently were eaten, and indeed frequently appeared on the public markets. That is certainly not so today. But whether this dis-appearance of Sirenian flesh is the result of a change of taste, with a rise in the standard of living bringing other more favoured meats into the reach of more numerous hungry people, or a decrease in the availability of mermaids to be killed, cannot be accurately assessed. Probably both factors are important. Whether the passage of recent protective legislation[1] has been influential must indeed and most sadly be doubted. We all know that legislation is only as influential as the power and the will to enforce it. The usefulness of legislation to protect a particular species is likely to be frail indeed when senior officers in the actual department of government concerned in its promotion are in fact ignorant of its existence.

Be that as it may, indubitably few manatees now reach the public market in the cities. It is unlikely to be found in Georgetown hanging from that telegraph pole near Penitence Market where 'bush-meat', tapirs and other mammals, may regularly be bought. In the past, New Amsterdam was the chief market for manatee meat, probably because the creatures were more abundant in the rivers of that region than elsewhere. That is not true today. The market overseer and the chief butcher—both expectedly or quite reasonably ignorant of novel legislation—see now no more than about one in two months pass through the market and their hands. Are people become abiders by the law, or are the animals much fewer than before? Sadly, the latter is more probable.

The meat of manatees is said to be of three qualities, textures or tastes, one like beef, one like poultry and one like fish. But just how these separate kinds are distributed about the body—cloaked in skin—seems to be information which cannot be extracted by mere question and answer. One must face the fact that throughout the world, and with the best will in the world, much information can never be extracted by question and answer from untutored people—or certainly not without a quite inordinate expenditure of time whose value exceeds that of the detailed information being sought.

Nor can the enquirer now appropriately go and slaughter a

1 Fisheries (Manatee Control) Regulations 1961 under the Fisheries Ordinance 1956. See Appendix I. p. 165.

manatee for the mere convenience of tasting it. So that other source of information, of personal experiment, is out of court. The natural death of a manatee is likely to take place unnoticed, but the unnatural death of one almost took place in such a way that her body would have yielded much to science. She was a huge female brought in by one who knew not well the law—a matter in which he resembled the whole population with a minimum of exceptions. He had hoped to sell her alive for export to a distant zoo, a project which was stultified both by an officer of the law threatening to take action and by the evident fact of her extreme sickness. Poor thing, she had been dredged from her river home and carried miles bouncing on a tractor. She was placed in a muddy pool to recuperate and there her tormented writhings were horrible to see. When she ought to have sunk her head and tail to leave her back exposed at the surface, she was bowed the other way and inverted, her broad belly to the sky, awash in mud and slime. There she rolled for days in seeming agony, at intervals raising her inverted head for air, then with heaving effort righting herself for a bare few seconds. That manatee we hoped would die, a hope based both on humanitarianism and on scientific zeal. The latter would have included the cooking and tasting of the meat from several parts of the body, in addition to exploratory dissection and the gathering of specimens. In the event, however, she was too tough, too tenacious of life, and she recovered slowly, later to continue her life in a pleasant pond in the waterworks.

Quite certainly the combination of mermaid personal elusiveness, their probable considerable decrease in numbers over decades, and the substantial distances to be travelled, made the search for sight of them not easy. These animals, living widely scattered in turbid waters in a novel country with few suitable boats and too much internal political seething —to say nothing of riot and fire—are not easy to discover.

Inevitably much—the most part—must be learnt by questioning and then integrating the answers. Such procedure is by no means to be condemned, more especially when there is no feasible alternative other than the passage of very much more time than can possibly be available. Nevertheless deliberate search for information may frequently result in the visitor in quite a short time in a new land seeing far more of it geographically than all but a few of its normal inhabitants. That certainly was so in our search for the mermaids themselves and for the details about them.

Such search—time never being unlimited—has its frustrations however much we may try to avoid them, however much we may cultivate a tranquil mind, tolerant alike of idiosyncracies of others and the inevitable failings of machinery. So often too much has to be attempted in too great a hurry. That is a 'European'[1] failing which has many causes, some rational and some just silly. Other people in other lands about the world, to us, often seem to have but little sense of time—except in connection with desired increases of material standards of living and of political change, and certainly not in connection with rapidity of reproduction. Travel enough within the time available; the need for speed, that is often an unavoidable evil.

Now sadly it happens that apart from Rolls Royces and electric canoes and marathon bicyclists, any increase of speed—well though it may be needed to reach distant places within time allowable—inevitably seems to lead to an increase of noise. When the speeding launch, with big outboard engine and overburdening drone of power, with spray flying and deafening mechanical tumult, dashes past the Hoatzins feeding

1 A United States administrative official among the Indians of Alaska would use the adjective 'Caucasian', which is perhaps after all more sensible.

on the creek side mocca-mocca, and the green parrots screech and flee in terror, then frustration is considerable if you have never met these fascinating creatures wild before. Egrets and herons crowding in their riverside rookeries swirl away like snowflakes before a blast; gay Jacanas, lily-trotting gems of pertness, run madly from the banks; quietly resting alligators plunge into the impenetrable depths; and more miles are gained before breakfast. These things are inevitable if particular places are to be reached in hours rather than days. Yet frustration undoubtedly grows in the breasts of those who have never before seen these particular pleasures of this fine new tropic land.

Speeding boat and secretive manatee are definitely allergic to one another. Yet the speeding, noisy, engined boat is essential if one is to reach the haunt of the mermaids within the limited weeks of Sabbatical terms. There is much that is inevitable and this seems part of it. One day, perhaps, with light fibre-glass hull and long-life batteries, the advanced electric canoe will enable fast travel which will compromise sufficiently between speed and silence. Yet the temptation of speed, like the temptation of power, is very great. Kindness too helps temptation, for much speed springs from kindness, the desire that the visitor shall see much and understand more in times made short by the advancing impetus of modern life.

So speeds the boat up, then down, the mangrove and mocca-mocca fringed creek, through the savanna and through the forest, which truly seems impenetrable, to man at any rate if not to a slim dog. Bend after bend is rounded, the boat's wash splashing upon the splaying roots and wetting the flanged buttresses which support the waterside trees. A bird's screech is inaudible, bright flowers are glimpsed momentarily, the alternating pattern of deep shadow and sunlight dazzles discernment. All are intent upon the homeward run after a day of novelty and not a little wonder. The engine roars, the boat skims, the people are silent, peering, steering, and the tacubas, the wooden snags, lurk beneath the surface.

Disaster comes in a single second; a knock and a crash and a hard wood prong rises through the boat's bottom; the man in the bows has taken a toss into the creek ahead, simulating those falling heroes of the Grand National steeplechase; another near cracks his ribs, another her arm, another is concussed and the split finger of the last provides the only blood which is spilled. From twenty m.p.h. to stillness in a moment; from mechanical roar to utter silence in that same moment; from a dry and loaded boat to a water-filled wooden dish in seconds. The silence of desire has come, yet in a manner unsought, by a means deemed improbable, and within seconds whose dangers have proved so happily less than some might previously have prophesied. The boat fails to sink completely, being held like a fishbowl upon a wooden stand; the creek is narrow; and those terrifyingly predaceous fishes, Pirais, happily are not hungry or not here. One swims ashore immediately and clambers in mud among the vertical stems. These he can just bend and break to begin to form a horizontal semi-floating shelf from which a first lodgement may be gained on what may more nearly be called the bank, impenetrably bushed though that remains.

Wits are soon collected enough to begin the passing ashore, through stream and mud, of that baggage which the boat contains—some little food, cameras and binoculars snatched from the rising water, clothes and other things. Prospects are not immediately easy to assess; there are many miles of creek without any habitation; recollection of distances passed in seconds of speed are not easily converted into distances of unmechanical human exertion. The tide ebbs and two valiantly set off to swim upstream against it on the chance that the memory of one is accurate, that the distance to a charcoal burner's shack is not too great. The all important cutlass is discovered deep underwater in the submerged bows of the boat and is got ashore. Then the mocca-mocca stems can be slashed and laid down to form a corduroy platform, even a lowly resting place such as male anthropoid apes are reputed to make on the ground while their smaller and more agile females climb into the branching tree above. The cutlass, too, seems a protection from whatever anacondas, boas or other great serpents, are ignorantly or accurately fancied to lurk in the vicinity. The expectation of a night spent in muddy squalor grows as the sun sinks and mosquitoes multiply.

A period of anxiety for the safety of those who swim—so slowly against the ebb and out of sight—is happily vanquished by a shout and soon the appearance of a dugout canoe with the swimmers and two dark paddlers, the charcoal burner and his boy. The rescued rum bottle plays its part. The ship-wrecked rise in spirits. The charcoal burners fetch a larger dugout which then is loaded with the precious, but newly useless and silent, outboard engine, all the gear and the thankful people.

Darkness now has come and soon the moon rises; the insects hum; birds, frogs, and beetles squeak, chirp and click; those who can paddle do so silently; the bush is alive and watches the foolish former speedsters again trying to speed with paddles and ebb combined. They paddle steadily for two hours and a dozen miles, stimulated by a bottle of gin which passes up and down the long, thin boat, themselves still dripping dankly, talking gently, sometimes joking, and one pondering the sad and seemingly unavoidable marriage between speed and that noise which spoils so much.

Speed and noise, rush and bustle, make the observation of mermaids in the mud quite impossible, yet such speed is un-avoidable to reach the places where the observations may with usefulness begin. The evil must be perhaps accepted in the hope of achieving, later, the objective. Silent electric canoes would be the ideal, for visiting zoologists and for all who would observe and learn in peace.

The river navigation of the Guianas is inevitably varied and the chance of seeing manatees while under way is thin indeed. The huge, dark, turbid rivers are plied by vessels and ferries appropriate to their size and importance. Large vessels, the carriers of sugar, bauxite, timber, oil, may go inland until the first rapids prevent their further progress. Such vessels move at ten to fifteen knots, with all the usual throb of large engines and big propellors. Launches with supplies move further inland bearing, in addition, missionaries, balata-gum bleeders and small cultivators, geologists, schoolteachers and mid-wives. Such launches go more slowly and the manatees may be less afraid, yet the slightest fear at once stimulates their invisibility. The dugout canoe, the paddled corial, is doubtless the best, because quietest, mode of seeing the manatees in their proper haunts. But the area observable is very limited unless the time available is the reverse—and that it hardly ever is. The use of the fast small launch, the cockle-shell speedboat, is one way of attempting compromise between distance great and time limited. All compromises inevitably have their dis-advantages, that being of their very nature: in this case it is the substitution of impression for detail visually, plus the danger of chance wreck upon invisible submerged snags. But the per-spectives and impressions gained are so very educative and fascinating that few will mind the dangers: they will simply insist on certain precautions for next time.

There are inevitable snags at any date and age. The old-time traveller was terrifyingly beset with biting insects and irritations in tropics and arctic alike, in the wet tropics all the year round, in the arctic the insects concentrating their attacks

in summer and being repulsed absolutely by low temperatures
for the rest of the year. The old-time traveller must have had a
constant fear of these plagues and pests and the fevers which
they bore, fevers which have now so largely been conquered
by the advance of modern sanitation and medicine. The modern
traveller in the Guianas, for example, unless exceedingly
unlucky, can expect no ills from malaria, yellow fever and
filariasis. Knowledge of the life histories of the parasites, of
the antidotes and practices which kill them at large, and of the
drugs which kill them in person, make his passage a pleasure
where his antecedents suffered cruelly. Examine the tomb-
stones and plaques in the churches and be thankful of things
as they have become today.

Yet there are new frustrations for the modern traveller,
frustrations of quite a different and most wearying kind.
Leaving aside bureaucracy, and speed, and noise, take optical
equipment and sweat. I will explain.

In relation to oneself the optical dance almost leads to madness. The muddy-backed manatee with its fringe of green algae
lies contentedly in water at a temperature more salubrious
than the fiery sun will allow above. Examined it must be with
binoculars; photographed it must be on to moving celluloid.
The modern traveller, if he would do his duty to family,
posterity and science alike, is girt about, almost laced, with
leather straps supporting items of optical equipment. There
are binoculars to aid his personal sight—probably spectacles
besides to say nothing of false teeth, eyes and hearing aids—a
camera to take still pictures and like as not an exposure meter
as well. Then there is a ciné camera to catch the things which
run and fly and swim in wind and water, together with a bag for
more and more film and lenses and filters, and notebooks to
record where memory inevitably will fail. Soon one feels that
madness must come in as the sweat pours out. The bald head

needs a hat for protection and scanty eyebrows fail in their function as eaves to the eyes so that sweat runs into them and spills on to the spectacles. To use a camera the hat must be unstuck from the hot forehead, pushed back and probably blown off; the spectacles must be pushed up instead on to the same hot and slippery forehead which has for this purpose insufficient brow-ridges; and the eyepiece of the instrument must be peered through. By that time the surreptitious, silent and secretive manatee will have withdrawn itself into the turgid depths, or the rare bird will be in Venezuela. Additionally the camera must be adjusted according to a greatly changing light with the rapid passage of clouds across a brilliant sky, and the objective of all the effort probably has re-emerged at an unanticipated distance so that further search and focusing is needed with eyes now deprived of their normal bifocal spectacles. One gnashes one's teeth, real ones, with annoyance and frustration. And the same shifting of hat and spectacles is needed to use binoculars which are slung for convenience higher up one's chest. At any rate these binoculars are unlikely to be misted by condensation as is the trouble in polar travel. That little difficulty, one overcame by hanging the binoculars—probably needed after deliberation and with less than tropic speed—inside the top of one's outer garment. There, hanging on one's chest close to the skin, they remained warm so that breath would not mist them in use. Lady travellers will understand that for them a short telescope or monocular hangs more comfortably.

The optical equipment now seemingly necessary to the observant traveller, learned or youthful alike, becomes increasingly more burdensome, and flamboyant too. The extreme adolescent example is reached with the girls from private schools in Australia visiting the koala bears in Sydney Zoo. They are so bedecked with cameras still and cameras moving, that they seem criss-crossed with leather and beaded with lenses. Spectacled and bulging they are possessed of optical opportunity far in advance of their skill to use it. But, the cynic will remark, it all helps that trade which is now the whole world's merry-go-round.

Where koala bears provide perfection in their visibility and stillness in sunshine, the mermaids in their mud thwart the would-be photographic recorder in every possible way—by their invisibility, by their movement beneath the turbid waters, by their nostrils rising surreptitiously in the shadows. Yet, however frustrating for the zoological observer, those very features are the ones which indubitably save the lives of mermaids in a wicked world. Without those characteristics the prospects for mermaids would be dim indeed.

2

⌁⌁⌁⌁⌁⌁⌁⌁⌁⌁

Prospects for Mermaids

APART FROM alleged and occasional struggles with alligators, the manatees have no evident predators other than
men, at any rate once the hazards of birth are overcome. But
everywhere predation by men is a factor which commonly
increases continuously until the predator has destroyed the
possibility of further prizes, for the prey are all gone, extinct
or so rare that hunting ends. Until a few centuries ago the
Guianas were occupied by no more than a few thousands, or
maybe tens of thousands, of Amerindians hunting with bows
and arrows, traps and nets. A few of their descendants still do
the same today. Their hunting of manatees and other food
species were, over so wide an area, supportable by the stocks
of creatures available. Since then, however, new men have
arrived from afar, and have multiplied enormously, particularly in the coastal strip and along the rivers of manatee-land.
By the beginning of this century there were about a quarter of
a million of them, while now there are nearly three-quarters
of a million. And, having about the highest rate of population
increase in the world—an impediment which may well lead
them to disaster if not subdued—they are likely to double in
number again in less than twenty years. Now, too, they no
longer use bows and arrows but guns. Though they are

mainly engaged in agriculture rather than hunting, they travel the rivers progressively more disturbingly in ships and fast powered boats. Many species of animals feel desperately the new pressures. Many species of animals may well soon not survive, so leaving the Guianas, and the world, a poorer place, less interesting[1] and exciting, with less variety and less usefulness as well. In these problems the Guianas are merely symptomatic of a disease of the world at large where in so many areas, more especially tropical areas, striking and attractive animals are suffering from man-pressure almost or quite to extinction. So the furnishings of our world are progressively destroyed, and we leave it for our children and our further successors a worse and not a better place.

Yet, in large degree, this despoliation and damage to longer term human interests is not inevitable: it can often be avoided by a sufficiency of forethought and good sense. Man-pressure need not utterly destroy: when re-directed men can preserve and conserve other creatures to their mutual advantage—and manatees among the rest. It is short term interest, based on biologically-divorced, unrealistic and often urban life which is the cause of countrywide destruction—that and the mere natural pressure for food from the multitude. Yet it is urban fecklessness on holiday which is most stupid and irrational of all.[2] Some may wrongly and ignorantly feel that all this is

1 The British Guiana Museum in Georgetown, under the leadership of Mr Vincent Roth, and the Surinam Museum in Paramaribo, directed by Dr Geijskes, are the chief centres of local interest in faunal preservation and conservation.

2 Even North Americans, now the leaders in conservational effort after immense earlier despoliation of their own habitat, still exhibit examples of the most wretched kind. The shooting of bears, with the aid of helicopters, in Alaska and the Aleutian chain of islands is one. Where hunting is more rationally controlled the sportsmen often have to wear bright red hats so as not to shoot each other in the short and highly intensive open season for deer.

merely the biologist grumbling at fate in this our day and age. But that is not truly so: it is perfectly possible, by taking thought, to preserve and to conserve other species of animals and plants worldwide, and to our own advantage.

'Preservation', in modern biological parlance, means saving from destruction, keeping in existence. 'Preservation' is a limited concept involving perpetuation and future existence and little more. 'Conservation', on the other hand, is a much wider concept going beyond mere 'preservation'. 'Conservation' includes regular and deliberate use by harvesting a crop —of animals or plants—on a rational long term basis, such that the breeding stock remains unimpaired while the natural increment by growth and reproduction alone is taken to serve man's ends. All normal farming throughout the world, both as to plants and as to domestic stock, is strictly 'conservation' of the species concerned. Not to conserve is to eat the seed corn, or to kill the goose which lays the golden eggs. Yet perhaps there are many now so urban, so divorced from reality, that those figurative aphorisms have no meaning.

In British Guiana the prospects for animals which are both visible and slow are very bad. Their chance of avoiding individual and specific extinction seems at present thin. Take the Hoatzin, or Canje pheasant, that curious bird with certain strange primitive features like the claw on the wing with which the young one climbs. This zoological rarity occurs now only in a few limited areas of a special botanical type. They inhabit only a particular vegetational zone which itself is of small extent and only occurs on the banks of a few of the main rivers, and that fairly near their mouths. These extraordinary birds, long-legged and, in imagination, a hybrid in shape between a large hawk and a crow, seem slow and clumsy as they tread the twigs and bending mocca-mocca stems growing in that intermediate verge where land and tidal river meet. They stand about two feet tall and weigh about seven pounds. They might, impolitely, be called avian stumble-bums, so curious is their gait among the branches usually ten or twelve feet above the water and very visible. Their nests hang over the water and are equally visible. The birds being large and slow and obvious are extremely vulnerable; they rarely take flight. The Hoatzins are utterly harmless and they are not even palatable, being often referred to as 'Stinking Hannahs'.

Who then harms the Hoatzins? The answer, we were assured, is that they are killed by Seventh Day Adventists. This statement, for the Canje river at any rate, may well be true. But in fact and of course Seventh Day Adventism incorporates no curious Hoatzin-cult requiring the slaughter of Canje pheasants. The facts are sadly more simple than that. The limited botanical environment in which the Hoatzins live, on the Canje river, chances to be within the area evangelized by zealous Seventh Day Adventists whose flock, in this respect, are the biological sinners.

The rivers are the main channels for movement from the coast inland, and the number of power-boats and the possession of guns both rapidly increase. That, some will regard, is a proof of a proper increase of the standard of living—or is it the expectation of death?—for the few. The result is that the Canje pheasants, vulnerable at all times, are now more subject to the depredations of those who stupidly shoot for fun. Like many other creatures in the Guianas, and elsewhere in the world, the Hoatzins are shot for no other reason than the desire to shoot[1] by feckless uneducated people with the strength to pull a trigger. The birds are not picked up nor eaten, but

[1] There is an extant Wild Birds Protection Ordinance dating from 1919, but in practice it is totally ineffectual in protecting any species of birds.

simply fall victim to those who shoot at anything that moves. In justice to the river-dwelling people of B.G., and the gun-carriers who rush from Georgetown at the weekends, they have their stupid equals scattered over Europe, and the United Kingdom too, where the greater opportunity for education makes the shooting even more inexcusable.[1]

Now, it is believed, no more than a few hundred—very dubiously two or three thousand—Canje pheasants remain alive in the Guianas of our day. They are in grave jeopardy of final local extinction within a very small number of years, and that entirely through the folly of local people.[2]

[1] From the Cameroons in recent days comes news of growing affluence—the gun replacing bows and arrows. Even the remaining gorillas are now being destroyed and eaten. The older people say they 'taste very good, just like men'.

[2] Dr J. Lear Grimmer, Associate Director of the National Zoological Park, Washington, D.C., has a special knowledge and experience of the Hoatzins after two or three visits in recent years. He has done much work investigating their food habits and physiology in the hope of finding a technique which will enable their successful maintenance and breeding in captivity. That is a most important possibility.

It is believed that the Hoatzins are now limited to the following rivers in the Guianas taking them in order from east to west. Possibly present in the Nanniecreek but otherwise not known to exist in Dutch Guiana (Surinam). There are a few in the Canje Creek (river); a few in the Berbice river; a few in the Abary river; a slightly greater number it is said in the Mahaicony river. There may possibly be some—but of this there is no detailed evidence—in the region between the Pomeroon river and the Venezuelan border. The total number in B.G. is said to have got markedly less in the last few years, and cannot now exceed a few hundreds. They occur too in parts of Brazil and Venezuela, and even perhaps west as far as Colombia in limited areas. Everywhere, because of their nature, they are potentially most vulnerable, even if in places their decline has not yet started. Venezuela reputedly has the largest residual stock of Hoatzins, but their safety must remain problematical even there.

Now return to the manatees. Their main immediate danger in the Guianas, probably it may be asserted with accuracy, is now the chance shot of the stupid, or sportive, human. Such people are progressively increasing in numbers as shot guns become more abundant. Such people in general are not patient and certainly not perceptive of the beauty and value of the local fauna. Speeding up the rivers they fire at any living target that may present itself. A flying ibis, duck, dove or toucan, will probably receive any attention that has wandered from the sitting Hoatzin as the boat speeds past. The head or nostrils of the manatee will probably be either invisible or spared unless nothing flies within range immediately the gun has been reloaded. Yet any shot which does find its mark in the manatee's nostril, the mermaid's nose, is liable to cause a disproportionate damage and, it may well be, lead to death. The nasal valves are of such essential importance to the creature that any damage which may allow early or later leakage may well result in drowning—and if not drowning a much increased vulnerability at the surface.

Rifles too, not only shotguns, also multiply virtually un-checked. These are used more deliberately, and with greater patience. Alligators, manatees and land mammals then are killed for fun or meat. But no evidence was actually collected in B.G. of the deliberate shooting of manatees with rifles, though it is not to be doubted that it does sometimes occur.

Nevertheless, in fairness to the gun-carriers of Guiana, wretched and stupid as are their actions, again, theirs are no worse than the actions of many in France and Italy, and juveniles in England too. The almost total absence of birds visible by day over so much of France is all too apparent to the discerning visitor. The number of guns in proportion to each surviving bird is surely higher in France than anywhere: just look around on Sunday mornings. An avian and mammalian desert is not difficult to produce.[1] The creatures of the Guianas are fortunate that as yet communications still are relatively poor and guns restricted by economics to the rather few. But the change already comes too rapidly.

Whatever may be the wretched fate which so closely besets the Canje pheasants, it would be wrong to suggest that the future of the Guiana manatees is yet equally as desperate. Fortunately it is not. The danger to the mermaids is real but so far they are largely protected by their elusive and surreptitious habits and mode of life—so unlike the seductive maidens of the myths. Nonetheless it is quite fair to say that their danger increases year by year. Study of them was, and still is, clearly desirable for so much about them remains unknown. At the same time the experimental approach is needed.

The prospects for manatees in the Guianas are weak enough to warrant varied efforts in parallel for their help. Preservation, in the sense of care and maintenance, in semi-domestication, is no new idea but is a real possibility. Nor is it a substitute for sensible conservation in the natural haunts— that conservation of course, where applicable, including rational harvesting. But in a wicked world it seems that frequently it will be, and often is already, wise to seek double assurance. Rational conservation in the wild and preservation

1 Piscine deserts, too are being produced elsewhere with the aid of an excess of aqualungers who wish to spear, not only look and enjoy. From the Mediterranean coast of France the large inshore fish are nearly gone: soon the little blenny will be the quarry of the much-accoutred sportsman. On some American sandy shores, old motor-cars are being dumped in shallow water to attract and provide homes for larger fish, so that the sportsmen will not return unconquering to shore. Sense this well may be, but the need is equally as squalid as the provision in London now of old cars in grimy asphalt areas so that there may be 'adventure playgrounds' for the urban 'under-privileged'.

by semi-domestication are not antagonistic in theory nor in practice. They simply represent two strings to one bow in the fight against extinction. There are examples enough to encourage much further comparable activity. The Ne-ne goose of Hawaii still just exists in the wild, a score or so of birds, but now by intensive effort the Wildfowl Trust's semi-domestic flock at Slimbridge and elsewhere is made up of several times as many individuals. Père David's deer, once a wild species, then the inhabitants of the royal paddocks in Pekin, would now be extinct had not the then Duke of Bedford collected together the remnant after the city's sack and brought them to Woburn. Now Père David's deer exists in several scattered herds in N.W. Europe and the U.S.A. Other examples could be quoted and many new opportunities must be seized. When one sees the rare Okapi, from the dark forests of the Congo, breeding in a gravel paddock in Paris and in the Bronx Zoo, New York, one must surely recognize the opportunities there may be to safeguard further species of the greater mammals from the depredations of the people in their lands of origin. Much will have been achieved if basic stocks can be continued by breeding in semi-domestication until such time as the cultural evolution of the people in the creatures' homeland has advanced enough for safety there. In these days all alternative methods of specific safeguard from extinction should be pursued, so increasing the chances of ultimate success.

The possibility of so helping the preservation of the fast diminishing Canje pheasants or Hoatzins has been already mentioned. The task is a particularly difficult one because of the specialized habits of those birds. The need to continue the experiments, already begun along these lines, is urgent, Better far that a few dozen Hoatzins should die in husbandry experiments, with a chance of ultimate successful breeding, than that all should await the shots of the ignorant in the bush

alongside the rivers of Guiana. Tapirs, too, and Giant Ant-
eaters as well, should be early on the list for preservation by
semi-domestication.

This same line of thought most certainly applies to our
mermaids, the manatees. Elusive as they are, with the added
safety that this trait provides, no one can properly envisage
their future in the wild with optimism. If absolute wild life
reserves could be set aside and properly policed that would
suffice. But in an area with virtually the highest rate of human
increase in the world, with all too strong internal tensions to
steal the time of politicians and leaders, with folly-shooting
rampant and still increasing, absolute reservations which are
successful are not to be expected. Semi-domestic breeding
stocks of manatees are an obvious need and proper goal, both
within the Guianas and without.

Manatees seem to be both catholic in taste and docile, and
the chances of regular breeding success under controlled conditions should surely be rated high. As with other species there
are doubtless certain environmental and dietary requirements
which must be discovered and provided before success will
come. But the prospects most certainly seem quite promising.
The warm waters of Florida combined with United States
affluence and zoological enthusiasm should surely be available
and suffice for that other sub-species further north.

Some may argue that successful breeding has already been
performed, in the Botanic Gardens in Georgetown B.G.
There, manatees have lived these past sixty years in ponds
open to the public gaze and public interest, and the creatures
have grown tame and feed from the hand. But the evidence of
actual breeding is slight indeed. Possibly there was breeding
forty years ago but no evidence suggests such happening in
more recent decades. Indeed, in the absence of reliable
records, in the possibility of new animals being brought in

already pregnant, it cannot be certainly stated that breeding there has ever happened. Probably, however, it did occur occasionally in the past. Quite certainly these tame mermaids are not a self-perpetuating stock and do not breed to-day.

Two particular adverse factors which may well be connected with this non-breeding may be mentioned. The one is the growing disturbance of the creatures, both by increased numbers of visitors in a rapidly growing city and by the proximity of motor cars and other sources of noise. The Georgetown Police Band is trained for the delight and stimulation of the human ear: it may have the opposite effect upon virgin mermaids and their potential mates. The other particular adverse factor—and there may well be many more— is the seeming dullness of the creature's diet. We have no evidence for this possible dietary inadequacy, but simply draw attention to a likely possibility. In the wild the manatees quite clearly have a varied diet, a bit of this and a bit of that, soft weeds and grasses, floating and standing, and probably of many species. The volume of food available presumably is never limiting except perhaps when the creatures wander into estuarine waters. But in the Botanic Garden ponds the manatees seem to receive nothing but rather dry grass from the near-by lawns, and that they receive in limited quantities day after day as year succeeds to year. The ponds in which they live have no vegetation of their own because it has been eaten years ago and the number of mouths will not allow new growth. Disturbance and dry grass might well account for the lack of breeding for the last few decades. Additionally, or alternatively, it is possible that the animals may have all been of the same sex. Records are inadequate and nobody knows.

The paramount need is for careful and sensible attempts to

breed the manatees in private ponds. Food must be adequate, disturbance minimal, the physical conditions varied in the sense of deeps and shallows, slopes and little bays, and records must be properly kept after stocking with a known number of manatees assuredly including both sexes. All this seems obvious enough.

It is possible that the breeding requirements of manatees are much more complicated, including, perhaps, migrations between saline and fresh-waters, gregarious forms of courtship, specific foodstuffs and so on. Of all such possibilities we are at present totally ignorant. Meanwhile the attempt should be made in quiet and private ponds. Experiments should be made deliberately both with single pairs and with groups to see if breeding can be stimulated under relatively confined and controlled conditions. Special efforts should be made to provide a varied diet, adequate it must be hoped both in quality as well as quantity. If the experimental ponds are small then the majority of the food must be added, while if the ponds are large enough there may be full reliance on natural growth and availability. Much experimental work along these lines is needed. Ingenuity, care and proper records and observations are needed, not the expenditure and equipment required for almost all research in the physical sciences.

Once a breeding stock becomes available, then will come the time for export and experiment elsewhere, so as to prove over a wider field the potential economic use of the manatees both as magnets for the public in zoos and as savers of labour in weed clearance. With present knowledge and experience every catching of a manatee in the wild results in very substantial risks of early death, and certainly—so far—of virtual sterilization.

As yet in truth there is profound ignorance of almost all details of manatee breeding biology. Not even the period of gestation[1] is exactly known, nor the period of lactation, nor the age or size when breeding starts, nor the rate of growth, nor the expected length of life. A tremendous amount remains to be learnt and, with increasing scarcity, the opportunities for discovering the details rapidly grows less from year to year.

When the desire is to study in detail the breeding biology and growth of a particular species of mammal, the easiest basic method, apart from a final veneer of field observation, is to have access to a large number of dead ones. Sad as this may be it is the ideal method, more especially if the carcases are available in fair numbers, month by month, throughout the year. Thus has been studied, particularly within the notable 'Discovery' Investigations, the breeding biology of the greater whales, though the limitation of the whaling season to a few months has been an inconvenience. Thousands of whales, pulled up on to the flensing platform, whether ashore or afloat, have been measured, have had their ovaries or testes pickled and sectioned, have had their wax ear plugs[2] examined, their vertebrae sectioned and so on. Now we know in very considerable detail, for several species of the greater whales, their breeding cycle, their period of gestation, their rate of

1 J. C. Moore in *Journal of Mammalogy*, Vol. 32, No. 1, 1951, gives 152 days as a minimal figure for gestation in 'The Status of the Manatee in the Everglades National Park, with Notes on its Natural History'.

2 In the greater whales it has been shown that the wax plug provides a method for the determination of individual age. In the passage of time, from year to year, with changes of season, activities and food supply, wax is laid down to produce a plug which may be likened to a stack of ice-cream cones. If you cut that stack across you may count the years (as you may count the rings of growth in trees and in the scales and otoliths of fish), and so learn the years which have elapsed in the lifetime of the whale. Whether likewise can be discovered the age of a manatee is yet unsure.

growth, their expectation of life. Hence it has been possible to calculate the probable size of the total population of the species—within certain limits—and to declare with a sufficiently convincing if not persuasive accuracy the rate of harvesting which would be rational. In fact of course, as with the great majority of the developed piscine fisheries of the world, gross overfishing has occurred already for long, so that now more and more effort is put into catching fewer and fewer whales and the failure of the fishery is in sight.

Likewise with a variety of species of seals, Elephant Seals at South Georgia, Fur Seals at the Pribilof Islands, Sea Lions in the Falkland Islands, and other species elsewhere, the regular killing in a commercial fishery has been taken as the opportunity for a detailed study of population and breeding biology and of individual growth rate and length of life. Where the animals can be made to carry long-lasting marks, as with the dated aluminium darts fired from shotguns into the backs of the whales, or the hog ear tags clipped into the fore-flippers of thousands of Fur Seal pups, the data yielded at death has still greater useful significance.

With my own Weddell and Crabeater Seals in Antarctica, now nearly thirty years ago, we were killing the creatures to feed ourselves and our sledge dogs. We killed about 550 seals in all of which I killed three-fifths myself and, with kind help, was able to take a sufficiency of measurements, pickle gonads enough, take skulls aplenty, so that the breeding biology was properly deducible. Later evidence has importantly added to the picture but the basic work was done. But, as yet, with so many of the greater mammals of the world, our detailed knowledge is thin in proportion to what it ought to be. Now today, at last, when already 90 per cent of Africa's big game has been slaughtered within the last six decades for sport or under man-pressure, special research effort is being made to work out the letailed biology of several species. All the elephants, buffalo, ions and antelopes killed in Africa in the last half century have rielded in fact astonishingly little in detail, partly through ack of interest and partly through the wide dispersion of the cilling process. What is needed is one man, or one team of piologists, with access to many animals, both living and dead, hroughout the year in a single place. Fortunately at last, hough so sadly belatedly, such biological studies are now inder way in East Africa, largely supported by the Nuffield foundation and others.

In this light consider our mermaids in their mud, the nanatees of the Guianas. The total of knowledge in fact is rifling; however many manatees have been or are being illed, they are killed in scattered places, privily if the law is ecognized. The old days, when several manatees might be aid out entire side by side in a single day in the New Amster-lam market, now are gone. Whether they are gone because he stock of manatees is so much diminished, or whether the ule of law is influential, it is hard to say. Probably the answer s both. But certainly the opportunity to dissect, to take varies and skulls for purposes of research now is gone. This nay not be true somewhere in Amazonia, but we have yet to nd the place. In Brazil, where good sense and, seemingly, the ule of protective legislation alike are minimal, it may be that semi-centralized slaughter of manatees still continues. Certainly there was still a regular export of their skins so late s 1945.[1]

So it has come about that now today the study of the breed-ig biology of the manatee is extremely difficult in the absence f more than very occasional dead ones for investigation.

1 See 'O Peixe-Boi da Amazônia' por Nunes Pereira. Técnico a Divisâo de Caça e Pesca do Ministério da Agricultura. Imprensa)ficial. Manaus 1947.

There are the measurements and a record of the sex of a few score which have been obtained alive for experimental use by the B.G. Dept. of Drainage and Irrigation for weed clearance in canals. There are a few skulls, mostly without further details except sex and origin, scattered in museum collections throughout the world. And that is almost all.

Another method of studying any species of animal is to keep it alive in captivity, to induce it to breed and rear its young, and to breed again, all under careful observation as the creatures grow, mature and die. That has never yet been done with manatees so far as can be discovered. Indeed there is no record known to us of the mermaid ever having given birth in captivity under conditions providing information even as to the real length of gestation. All this is sad, stupid and frustrating, but there it is. Like an admirable sermon heard preached in St Paul's Cathedral in Dunedin to an astonishing congregation of antipodean Orangemen in full array, interest in the past is one thing, but what really matters is the future. That is very true of the conservation and study of the manatees of the Guianas today. We have collected what we can of evidence from the past, including the recollections of men and women of discernment. We have become all too well aware of the difficulties of detailed research today. We have an ardour which we would instil into others, for the proper care, conservation and use of the remaining manatees for the future. These creatures undoubtedly have genuine economic worth within the country's future, for their value in weed clearance, for their value in occasional sales to zoos and other purchasers overseas, and for their part in attracting the money from the pockets of interested tourists.

More especially in this absence of the possibility of killing large series of manatees, the extended study of the individual is essential for the unravelling of many features of age, life ınd growth. Yet, for that, one must be certain of the individual. He will not answer to calls of Tom or Bill, or even Bacchus or Luckhoo. Any special features, like wounds or scars, may disappear in time, and length will change. What is needed in such studies is an indelible and sure reference so that the ındividual may be recognized with certainty tomorrow, next week, next year, even a decade hence. That problem has been successfully met in other species, of whales and seals and other creatures in many lands. But the problem of the manatee is much more difficult and yet awaits solution by the ingenious. Direct transfer of method from seal to Seacow is not possible ınd that for reasons which are valid.

The traditional method of marking cattle, and human creatures too who were guilty of lies or fraud or misdemeanours of many kinds in ancient days, was branding with a heated iron. It is cruel and clumsy, effective and permanent. Many terrestrial domestic animals still suffer it in the world today. Many seals, too, have been branded and have carried the scars for years for the convenience of biologists—a big bull Fur Seal carried the mark for thirty years. Elephant Seals and Sea Lions, and many others too, have felt the searing redness of the iron and have thereby provided later evidence of growth, age and breeding habits.

Yet for manatees this method, though never so far as I know attempted, is almost certainly useless. Branding requires heat and apparatus and is only convenient when many are to be branded in quick series at a herding together. Manatees are never available in such conditions: scattered ones and twos are no subject for branding. Further, release again into the natural habitat after branding would almost certainly result in two new hazards to the creature, the one, a rapid fungus infection, and the other, attacks by small predaceous fish feeding in the wounds. Such hazards are not for infliction upon the few manatees available for marking and later study.

This particular risk makes one ponder another one similar. At the birth of the young—usually a singleton though even of this there is no precise knowledge—surely there must be grave risk of attack by predaceous fishes, called together by the smell of blood and the presence of a soft umbilical cord. This hazard must certainly be avoided by one means or another. It suggests perhaps that the pregnant and full term manatee must resort to very special places, perhaps at special seasons, where this particular danger will be minimal. Yet again we have no knowledge.

To return to the possible modes of marking individual animals, there are others for description and assessment.

Ear clipping, notching or punching, is not for animals which have no ears save tiny slits whose visibility is near impossible. However the use of ear tags, that prevalent method of mark-ing cattle, sheep and pigs, has been extensively applied to seals, not indeed to ears inadequate for the purpose, but to flippers. The most successful position, as demonstrated by thousands of the small black pups of the Alaskan Fur Seal, is in the thin hinder, trailing, edge of the fore flipper, close up to the axilla. Such tags, of stainless steel and serially num-bered, have served their purpose of individual recognition for many years, just as have numbered rings upon the legs of now countless birds. But manatees are far from so accommodating The flippers have no convenient thin hinder edge: the flippers are thick and fleshy and have no shiny flap as conveniently in seals. The flippers of the mermaids, too, are used more as props and hooks for lifting and dragging: there is no security for any normal tag as used for seals. The proximity of the breasts in the females, additionally, makes the axilla unsuit-able for tags. A numbered bull ring in the tail is a possibility not yet tried. But the tail quite evidently is vulnerable alway to damage at its edge and one would fancy that no ring would hold for long.

A further possibility, which has proved successful with certain seals, for a few months at most and not as is desirable for years, is marking with colour. This we tried, using both some special dyes provided kindly by the Academic Relations Department of I.C.I. and some simple aluminium paint. We hopefully made gay the heads and noses of several manatees, painted the faces of the mermaids, first drying them carefully with towels. But all was to no purpose. Within two or three days colour had vanished, and it seemed that the grey skin is constantly sloughing its surface so that all colour, added or absorbed, is ephemeral. Possibly an expert in tattoo could solve the problem, needling white pigment numbers safe beneath the sloughing surface yet not so deep as to be invisible. That we had no opportunity to try.

Another potential method, as yet totally untried, would be the application of a coloured plastic and slightly elastic belt around the manatee, to fit the strong constriction where tail and body join. Doubtless, if successful, 'waspies for mermaids' would be the headline in that small section of the national press whose interest lies midway within the usual quadrangle formed by sport, politics, literary criticism and sexual crime. Such a close-fitting, coloured belt could carry numbers, should be permanent, and would be unlikely to catch on submarine snags. There is space within the constriction and yet behind the natural orifices.

Experiments such as this most certainly need trying so that an effective mode may be discovered of knowing the individual with sureness at much later dates.

Now preservation in semi-domestication, research on life cycles, and protection by proving usefulness can, with manatees, all run in parallel if proper efforts are made to that end.

To explain, we must describe in further detail the potential watery habitats in the Guianas. The run of the natural rivers has already been described, but additionally there are innumerable man-made channels in which the manatees may or might live happily. For a proper understanding it is convenient to begin by contrasting lowland coastal areas on the two sides of the Atlantic.

So, to begin, the middle of the City of Cambridge is no more than fifteen feet above mean sea level, and the river water, a few feet lower, has still a further fifty miles to reach the sea. The drainage of land and flood prevention become a natural interest for those reared in East Anglia, and indeed such matters ought to be the concern, and within the appreciation of, a large proportion of the world's population. A rise of sea level of as little as 100 feet world-wide would flood the living places of more than half the population of the globe. And a marginal shift in mean sea level is always a possibility. The melting of perhaps 70 per cent of the ice of Antarctica would be sufficient, though the time required might be substantial. The South-East corner of England has been sinking since Roman times at the rate of over a millimetre each year more than two whole metres in 2,000 years. But the surface of the drained fens of Cambridgeshire has sunk, through gradual drying of the underlying peat, at a far higher rate, so that much can happen within the lifetime of an individual. The result is the constant need to pump the water from the land drains up to river level. The dangers of flooding correspondingly increase.

The coastal lands of the Guianas, B.G. and Surinam alike are somewhat similar but more so. They resemble Holland in the need for dykes to restrain the sea and for special effort to shed any excess of land water. It was Dutch engineers with their special expertise in times past, who equally engineered the still prevailing drainage and coastal protection patterns in all these areas, homeland Holland, East Anglia and the Guianas. Like Holland, the Guianan coasts are walled by a continuous preventive bank to restrain flooding from the sea above half tide. An earlier polder system, the surrounding of limited areas by such banks, has been transformed by the confluence of adjacent polders to provide a continuous sea wall, between the mouths of the rivers. These huge rivers are in beds so flat that the tidal influence may run even a hundred or more miles inland. Between the salty rivers the fresh land water now escapes to sea by a system of channels which can only flow at lower than half tide, the tidal water being prevented from flowing inward by one-way sluices. These sluices are the kokers which are so typical of the Guiana coastal scenery. The kokers and the polders and the stellings[1] are all vestiges of most admirable Dutch endeavour.

Though the Guianan coastal plain is a watery place, it is also often in need of water. What is available in abundance is brackish water from the sea and from the tidal rivers, while productivity, sugar and rice production, require fresh irrigation water—and that is often in short supply. So has been developed a complexity of water arrangements—of conservation areas inland with long distributary channels to carry irrigation water to the cultivated coastlands—which may bewilder the newcomer.[2] The rate of evaporation is high, for the climate is warm but not humid, and rainfall varies much from year to year. Adequate water for the sugar estates and

1 Kokers are the sluices which separate the fresh water in the drained polders from the sea. Stellings are wharfs.
2 The best description and history of this subject is to be found in R. F. Camacho's 'General Review of Drainage and Irrigation in the Coastal Plain and Report for the years 1957, 1958 and 1959 on the Drainage and Irrigation Department', Georgetown, British Guiana. 1960

for the rice cultivators may often be a matter of some real anxiety.

A further pattern of complexity is added by the need, in sugar cultivation, not merely for irrigation water, but for drains to carry the residual water away. It is, as it were, an extension of this system which operates in irrigated arid Egypt, where, for several months in the year, virtually none of Nile's water enters the sea direct, there being nothing left but the residues pumped from the deep drains. In contrast the Punjab has, by report, irrigation channels but few drains so that salting by evaporation has become a constant problem.

The Guianan sugar estates are fed with irrigation water by distributaries from the conservation areas, or from the rivers above the influence of salt. This water commonly forms the 'middle walk' a relatively high level channel through the area of cane. From it feeder channels multiply. At a lower level the drainage water is collected by the 'side walks' which become confluent and run out finally via the kokers at the coast itself. The waterways of the sugar estates have, however, a further use. They are the lines of communication, the means by which the loaded cane punts are pulled to the factories by mules or tractors.

This pattern of waterways, as described, is often an over-simplification in reality. But here is enough to indicate something of the magnitude of the task of channel clearance in the face of fast-growing aquatic vegetation of many kinds in a tropic land. The costs of channel maintenance, so that water may flow freely and punts move nicely, are great. The high cost production of Guianan sugar is partly attributable to these intrinsic watery problems of the low-lying coastlands. This is the background to the experimental and suggested wide use of manatees for channel clearance, for the removal of aquatic vegetation as fast as it may grow. That is the hope. The reality has many difficulties. Nevertheless this extensive system of man-made waterways afford an enormous potential habitat for manatees. But the conversion of potentiality into actuality, as always and in so many walks of life, may be a most difficult, saddening or even impossible task—human nature being what it is.

The traditional mode of channel clearance, to counter the evergrowing weed, is the labour of men and women, cutlass in hand, waist deep and more in turbid water. There they work long hours with a cheerfulness which is a credit to their nature; they work long hours for weeks on end, for the total lengths to be cleared are enormous. Cutting cane in the crop season, a man may often be joined by his wife cutting weed in the alternating months. The weed cutting is a task only less arduous than the cutting of sugar by the fact that the weed does not have to be lifted in large bundles and stacked as does the cane. Hazard by snakes, both land and water, is certainly not absent. The fortune of the climate it is that the task of weed cutting is not made worse still through human chilling. The water is always warm enough to prevent that further hardship. The weed cutting is performed almost entirely by people of peninsular Indian origin who form today the great bulk of the labour on the sugar estates. It may well be that it was the sight and experience, of father and mother together struggling in this arduous toil, which has led the child, the politician of today, to a determination to strive for change and opportunity for his rural followers.

An alternative to weed clearance by man and woman power, is mechanization and the use of drag-line excavators adjusted to the task. This alternative has its snags however. Such machinery in use requires a sufficiently solid trackway along-side each water channel to be cleared, so perhaps doubling the area of unproductive land. Mechanization too requires the sinking of more capital, in this instance in a manner which will result in seasonal unemployment—however arduous may be the human employment which is replaced. The problem is far from easy of solution.

Other alternatives are everlastingly being tested. Temporary drying of channels may be useful, more especially if linked with treatment with modern weedicides—that hateful term. Here is more potentiality, but in practice there are substantial difficulties both in the killing of useful fish and in the fouling of waters upon which people may depend for normal use.

It was the need to face this problem of weed clearance which already decades ago, early in the century, led certain sugar estates to experiment with manatees in the walks and channels to see if they would at least help, if not perform, the essential weed clearance. The records are somewhat scant but it is quite evident that experiments were deliberately made in several areas.[1] The efforts proved abortive. A combination of human hunger for supplementary meat and the movement of cane punts was too much for these unpaid aquatic Sirenian toilers.

New attempts to enlist Sirenian effort in the clearance of channels has caught local public attention in Guiana in recent years, admirably stimulated by Mr Allsopp,[2] the Fisheries Research Officer. His proper zeal and enthusiasm, however,

---

1 Vincent Roth says 'this practise was adopted by practically every sugar estate before the turn of the century. Indeed Plantation Non Pareil had no fewer than twelve of these aquatic mammals for this purpose'. (Journal No. 29 of the British Guiana Museum & Zoo 1961.) No confirmation of this is now available, but more recent attempts were made in 1946 at Skeldon and in 1959–60 at Por Morant.

2 Letter to *Nature*, No. 4752, Vol. 188, November 1960, p. 762

have proved infectious to excess. The ill-judged optimism of others suggested a glowing future for the manatee in the perpetual clearance of floating vegetation, in the new man-made Kariba lake in Africa. That idea took the public fancy[1] almost throughout the western world, with the aid of a Press which showed more interest than discernment.[2] Theoretical and potential are truly the more accurate adjectives for des-cribing the possible use of manatees in Kariba, rather than mundane words like practical and probable and workable. Whatever may be the totally untried theoretical possibility, in fact the quantitative arguments overwhelm all chance, within a useful period of time, of helpful activity by Guianan manatees transported to Africa. The area of Kariba lake is so huge; the supply of manatees could not be great and they are very difficult and expensive to find and to catch; the breeding of transported manatees is very far from being assured; and in any event their multiplication, compared with the majority of mammals, certainly is slow. The idea was fascinating but the actuality is remote.

Yet lack of real potentiality in such exalted schemes must not detract from genuine possibilities of usefulness at home. Surely, one may legitimately ask and suppose, there is real usefulness to be derived from the vegetarian propensities of manatees in the myriad man-made channels of B.G.? Surely there are some instances in which they may replace the weary human cutlass bearers wading in weed and toil?

For manatees to live successfully in these man-made water-ways, for these mermaids to perform the beneficent task of

1 *Time* (Atlantic Edition), Vol. LXXVI, No. 25, p. 51.
2 The picture began to be restored to its proper perspective by he publication by F.A.O. of 'Some notes on the use of the Manatee *Trichechus*) for the control of aquatic weeds' in Fisheries Biology Technical Paper No. 13, Rome 1961.

saving human labour by eating the weed that otherwise fills the channels, two things are needed. The first is that the animals shall live and not be killed, and the second is that they shall breed there, so that the stock becomes self-maintaining without the need for constant importation from the wild. Mermaids quite particularly like a quiet life. They seek it, even if they don't altogether achieve it, with the aid of their typical elusiveness. But being without means of physical protection, elusiveness is not enough for survival in shallow channels more particularly when narrow. The temptation to seize meat for the chopping, in lands where every other hand carries a cutlass and where land meat is expensive, is often too great for long life and mermaid happiness.

Even if a chop is not the manatee's fate in constricted waters, and even if the local people appreciate the Sirenian effort to consume aquatic weeds, there certainly seems not to be peace enough for successful reproduction. Thus, so far, every catching of a manatee in the wild and placing it to work in weed-ridden channels, has been tantamount to sterilization. It is quite clear that their large scale use in such ways to save men labour is impossible unless they can be brought to breed in the state of semi-domestication. The catching of individuals in the wild is difficult and expensive; their transport is arduous and accompanied by not few losses; and the wild stock is far from inexhaustible.

To repeat the argument, efforts need to be made—and this is true of many of the larger species of animal in the wicked world of today—efforts must be made to produce semi-domestic breeding stocks of manatees and others as a mode of conservation and protection. That done the usefulness of these creatures might be widely extended in the distant future. But the essential adjective is 'distant', for here is no quick job. Much experiment is needed, and even if entirely successful it is likely that the mermaids will be found to be slow breeders. The detailed biological data in this regard is yet quite absent.

In seeking peace for mermaid nurseries it is of no use thinking that the waterways of sugar estates will suffice. That is certainly not so. The movement of heavy cane punts, which in fact occupy almost the entire cross section of many channels, is quite inimical to mermaid peace if not survival itself. Additionally, it may be, there are further most important relevant factors. Manatees, it seems, are great wanderers and to keep them in particular channels grills must be placed to restrain them. That often restricts navigation as well. But whether long distance movements are essential to manatee well-being and to the breeding cycle are unknown. Additionally, there is some evidence of manatee gregariousness. Whether the absence of that possibility, when confined in weed channels, will itself prevent or limit successful breeding, we simply do not know.

There are further difficulties and special arrangements which may be necessary before breeding can be successful. Small things count for much in a complicated cycle: not only diet must be adequate but sometimes detailed physical conditions as well. Take an example from the anthropoid world. It is now asserted that for successful breeding, indeed for profitable copulation, the physical requirements of certain apes are quite particular. In forests, amid trees and broken branches, precise conditions may be sought and found, which means branches conveniently placed and distanced for suitable handholds and footholds during actual copulation. Without such just right circumstances—and absence is the normal in captivity—breeding will not occur. Provide the facilities correctly and young will follow.

It may be that such a comparison is directly applicable to

the breeding of manatees. It may be that they require some special physical circumstances, perhaps some special gently sloping shallow underwater bank, so that mating may be successful. It may be that the channels in which so far, experimentally, the manatees have been placed have lacked suitable depths and slopes, for such channels are deliberately and for good reasons kept steep-sided and straight. Shallow embankments and gentle slopes are normally out of place in estate waterways and in distributaries.[1]

At any rate the fact remains that so far, apart from possibilities several decades ago, manatees have not bred[2] in captivity in ponds nor in the channels where they have been

1 Very recently a most interesting and important eye-witness account has arrived telling of the actual mating of manatees in very shallow water. This report comes through the good offices of Mr Arthur Goodland of Georgetown as told to him by the men who witnessed the event on 9 January 1955. The place was about thirty-five miles up the Abary river then in flood and the events recorded occupied $2\frac{1}{2}$ hours in the morning in full sunlight and in the absence of river traffic. It seems that the river was about two feet above normal level so that there was a shallow stretch about sixty feet wide where the water diminished in depth from two feet to nothing. The report says 'when first seen' the manatees 'were disporting themselves in the river towards the left bank, and in a school of fourteen to sixteen; they gave the impression of fighting among themselves. Later they moved into the shallow, and worked themselves up the bank into six inches of water, one pair was completely out of the water. Then they mated lying on their sides'. The report includes a most helpful sectional diagram of the left bank of the river at the point of interest. 'The above reported . . . by one of the three men (Archie Bunbury) who actually observed them, and had endeavoured to slaughter at least one of the manatees, they (the men) were afraid and stood three feet away. The three men were Archie Bunbury of Cottage, E.C.D., Alvin Percival of Cottage, E.C.D., and Withney Bernard of Regent Street, Georgetown.'

2 Though there may have been instances of a calf born to a cow already pregnant on arrival in the channel.

set to work. All manatee catching so far results in death or the equivalent of sterilization.

Experimental work is still proceeding in B.G., though it seems that the sugar estates have recognized that the manatee's efforts are not really applicable to their special problems and topographical circumstances. But governmental investigation and experiment is still sensibly in progress. It is interesting to follow something of its course.

Initially having been stimulated by the Fisheries Department,[1] over a period of about three years, some seventy manatees have been captured, almost entirely in the Canje and upper waters of the Abary rivers, an area of moist savanna. The capture is effected by a particular operator who has come to know the most convenient technique. The creatures are driven into shallow backwaters and there netted with a heavy seine stretched behind them. Time and effort and ingenuity are all required in this isolated region. The creatures are heaved struggling from the water and are then dumped in the bottom of a boat. Once clear of the water struggling, in general, is slight. The unfortunate manatee, now gravity-bound in contrast with its normal aquatic free support, suffers in stillness. Transport down the river for scores of miles takes many hours in a boat propelled by a small outboard engine. Travel in the heat of the day is avoided where possible and an occasional splash of water is thrown over the creature's head and body.

Arrived at the Abary Bridge or near it, the manatee is often held for a few days in a pond until convenient transport by road to Georgetown is available. Those last fifty miles over a road beset with stones and potholes—'mermaid-wise', as

1 Mr Allsopp, the Fisheries Research Officer, was the instigator who started the experimental work on sound lines; he has since been away from B.G. on secondment to Togoland.

doubtless now some would say in the modern idiom—must be most unpleasant for the creature bouncing on its belly, the impacts perhaps a little softened by a few wisps of straw or reeds. The animal is roped to prevent the bigger bumps being successful stimulants to renewed struggle. In earlier days the mermaids were transported in a water-filled canvas tank. But the water sloshing was excessive, and on one occasion a manatee leapt clear of the water to land heavily on the ground and die. The tale of that occasion is often quoted to enquirers all up and down the coastal road.

For all his pains and troubles the cheerful and ingenious Mr Geet Lal—to give him his planetary name, for he is Boop to his friends—receives from Government a sum in B.W.I. dollars for each manatee delivered alive in Georgetown. Once arrived there the creatures are handed over to the Fisheries Service and placed in trenches in the nether regions of the Botanic Gardens. There life continues for some few weeks in muddy shallow water, on a diet which must be much less pleasant than the lush weeds available in the wild. During the period in the Botanic Gardens a large dose is administered of anti-fungal pills,[1] by the simple expedient of wrapping the pills with weed and pushing them into its mouth while the creature lies quiescent out of water. Bruises, cuts and chafings of the skin are sadly inevitable in the course of catching, transfer and transport, and these are most liable to fungal infection with detriment to the mermaid. This anti-biotic treatment by massive dosage is said to counteract all danger from this source.

After a few weeks spent in these holding trenches in the Botanic Gardens the manatees are re-caught and re-transported by truck and handed over to the Drainage and Irrigation

1 The dose consists of 16 tablets (each of 250 mg.) of Griseo-fulvin.

Department and released where that department thinks expedient. From the Berbice Hand of the Abary River to the final channel, perhaps a distributary from a conservation area, may take weeks or months according to circumstances and enthusiasm and plans made and promises not kept.

So the experimental work *happens*; to use the word 'proceeds' would suggest an exactitude, a regularity and a recording of details which surpasses by far the truth.

Up to date about seventy mermaids have been captured in this programme, but of these it would seem that nearly half have certainly died, if an integration be made with those which succumbed soon after delivery at their final destination. Just as the softness of the cushion in the story defeated the sword that had severed a camel's head, so the later records of this manatee programme defeat attempts at elucidation. Even a new Saladin with his special sword of supreme sharpness would likewise be defeated.

In this programme there is room for much further improvement, not alone in documentation, transport and handling. If manatees are ever to prove that they can breed under semi-domestication, usefully in channels, like other mammals it is essential that males and females should be present together, in fact and not only in intent.

Despite all failings in the experimental programme, it does seem definite that in a few instances manatees have successfully kept particular lengths of channel clear of vegetation for periods of over a year. Apart from the obvious example of the main pools in the Botanic Gardens in Georgetown, where perhaps half a dozen animals have lived for years in a confined space and fed on thrown-in grass, there are two particular examples which convince. The first is the Water Works pools[1]

1 There are two pools about 150 by 15 yards and 250 by 15 yards. The depth is very variable. These pools have been kept clear since 1950 by three manatees.

in Georgetown which have certainly been kept clear by the browsing of a few manatees, so avoiding considerable inconvenience and almost constant clearing.

The second is the distributary running for several miles from the water conservation area into the back of Wales Estate on the west bank of the Demerara river. When a departmental overseer, who is actually on the spot and responsible, shows enthusiasm for his captive mermaids and shows in detail what they have done[1] then the visitor can both believe and see.

It seems evident that best success can come when a suitable quiet channel has first been cleared of weeds, both floating and standing, by man power in the standard way. If then the manatees, two or three together, are introduced and left undisturbed but confined by grids to a suitable length of channel, then they will by browsing effort prevent the re-blockage of that channel with weeds. However the number of places of quiet retreat, where boats and punts will not disturb, where people will not tease nor chop, and where wandering is conveniently preventible, are few in fact. But in those special places the manatees may certainly be judged to have practical usefulness. The probable and considerable length of life is a favourable factor in such use. But better still by far if the animals can be persuaded to breed successfully in such relative confinement.

To extrapolate, from the meagre and inadequate evidence, and calculate what mountains of unwanted weed a hundred or a thousand manatees might eat in a year of high endeavour—whether at home or in Kariba—is to pile Pelion on a grain of

1 The main Wales distributary, about 20 yards wide and 5 to 6 feet deep, was being kept clear for several miles by seven manatees. Also a narrower continuation of this channel was being progressively cleared by two manatees recently introduced.

sand. That stricture has however by no means prevented the performance of this quite impossible task.

What then are the real future prospects for the mermaids in the Guianas? Certainly, saved by their elusiveness and aquatic habit, they are in no immediate danger of extermination there like the Hoatzins. Certainly, too, it is fair to assert that man-pressure upon them increases despite the seeming absence of deliberate hunting. That man-pressure, through guns and disturbance, is likely progressively to magnify to their detriment. The gradual disappearance of the manatees might long be unrealized and unobserved. Their decrease in the Amazon basin seems well-attested by the decrease now of success in their hunting for leather and for meat. That is not to say that those which are sighted will escape the hunter's shot. The general hunter continues his trade when the specialist has gone through lack of quarry enough. Guiana, for manatees, has had few specialists but the marksmen multiply.

There are, in such circumstances, two approaches to long-term protection and preservation, the one educational, the other separational. As so often, here too, the approaches must certainly not be regarded as alternatives. In wisdom both should be pursued, both are rational, they are in no way antagonistic, and both approaches may have beneficial influence over a wide range of other species of animals and plants in addition. A third approach, that by legislation, is in practice and in isolation both negative and ineffective; this approach should always be regarded as an adjunct to either or both the other two. It is frequently an essential adjunct: through legislation power can be exerted if the will is there.

In principle the educational approach to faunal protection and preservation is superior but inevitably takes time and extended effort by many people at all levels. It depends upon an initial local will to succeed by education, and a will which must be maintained for years. The educational approach is an accumulative one and its effects, at any rate in the earlier stages, are only marginal so far as concerns the creatures to be protected from excessive man-pressure. The educational approach though slow, is however the ultimately essential way to progress and to the attainment of higher levels of rationality.

The separational approach is an expedient, often in fact an essential and unavoidable expedient. This approach is necessary for one or both of two reasons. A stock of animals—of which the Hoatzins of B.G. are an all too good example—may already have reached such a low ebb, before anything is done, that time is insufficient for education to exert its beneficent influences. There could, on the other hand, be occasions where education is sufficient to preserve from intentional physical harm but yet the press of interested observers would be too great for the well-being of the rare creatures to be preserved, or their particular habitat. Under such circumstances, physical separation of the creatures to be preserved from the generality of human kind is necessary. The initial requirements are the will and the power given by legislation. This is a further argument for special reserved, national parks, or call them what you will. The time factor does not necessarily obtrude itself in their initiation—given the will and the power.

The separational approach has the advantages of being immediately influential upon the prospects of that or those to be preserved, and of being subject to the will, zeal and initiative of the few who have become enlightened, without need to wait upon the educational progress of the generality of the population. Such an approach is to be regarded as an exercise in leadership rather than in dictatorship. It is in fact gradually—perhaps all too slowly—becoming the way of the modern world.

The present population surge, in Guiana as elsewhere, serves but to strengthen the argument for the immediate separational approach, while the educational aspects can follow in their time.

A further advantage of the separational approach is that outsiders, learned societies, individuals of eminence, charitable trusts and international organizations, can all play a helpful part. In particular they can initiate by persuasion; they can demonstrate by example; they can lend their prestige and their funds to the task. So may they encourage local leaders in emergent nations.

In this setting it must surely be clear that the future safeguarding of rare creatures and special habitats in the Guianas must be approached by the early establishment of special reserves. If that were done now there would be no decrease of present local amenity, only a check upon the feckless desire to kill or burn during the time it takes for education to prosper in the biological field. Yet at the same time the establishment now of reserves would immediately enhance prestige internationally and provide an asset with financial, money-earning, worth for the future. There is real opportunity here.

Accepting such thoughts and concepts as principles to be followed if possible, there are, nevertheless, certain practical points for more detailed consideration. For example the very elusiveness and difficulty of observing manatees—those features which aid them in the world today—are features which militate against their future usefulness as magnets for drawing money from the tourists' pockets. On the other hand the manatees have already proved, and should continue to prove, their usefulness as weed clearers. For this purpose they have monetary worth even though at present the number of

favourable opportunities in the B.G. waterways is not as great
as might be imagined in the first flush of enthusiasm. Yet, as
education proceeds, the safety of the creatures in the channels
will gradually increase and then, progressively, the opportunities for weed clearance by manatees will increase as well.
For any such programme, however, a prerequisite is that the
creatures must be brought to breed in semi-domestication. If
success with that is not achievable—as for example working
elephants have never regularly been bred in captivity but have
been taken from the wild for training—then the requirement
of large, purely wild, breeding reserve stocks is all the
greater.

In terms of practical politics, too, it is essential to recognize
that the maintenance of a few large, 'many species reserves' is
expedient in contrast with the setting aside of a larger number
of smaller 'single species reserves'.

In the simplest terms and in the B.G. setting, as example, it
is better to have a larger reserve or 'park' for the preservation
of manatees and Hoatzins and other interesting species,[1] than
several separate small areas, the one for manatees, another for
Hoatzins and so on. This is a general principle but special
local circumstances may well require a different solution to the
problem of the preservation of species whose ecological niches
are widely dissimilar. Once there is a definite local will to
retain and preserve the wild life furnishings of any land, then
ways can be found of integrating the various requirements of
the animals and the plants and the human population as well.
The problem of today is that of any holding operation,

1 Mammals are protected in the Kaieteur National Park, an area
of only 45 square miles in the 83,000 square miles of B.G. See
article on 'Wild Life Preservation in the British West Indies,
British Honduras and British Guiana' in *Oryx*, Vol. IV, No. 5,
1958, p. 332. *Oryx* is the Journal of the Fauna Preservation Society,
London.

striving to preserve until such time as education and understanding locally can play their proper parts.

The needs of the Hoatzins and of the manatees in this setting form an interesting contrast. For the preservation of the Hoatzin it is abundantly clear that there is immediate need for absolute control—which means protection from sudden death and disturbance—over some or all of those small special riverine stretches where the remnants of the stock still survive. That is a pre-requisite and, without that, education will be useless for the birds will be locally extinct too quickly.

On the other hand, educationally-produced regard for the well-being of the manatees might be sufficient protection in itself for these elusive creatures, even if that education takes a decade or two. Sensibly however, the educational effort should be paralleled by special care and control. In both instances the essential background, of theoretically protective legislation is already available—for the Hoatzins under the, in practice, defunct and elderly Wildbirds Act and for the manatees under the new rules[1] of 1961 whose existence is not yet well recognized. The actual implementation of this sensible existing legislation is essential: legislation—printed words on paper—is useless, unless the Courts, having the power, in fact convict and punish.

1 See Appendix I.

3

~~~~~~~~~~

Seacows of the World

'GENTLEMEN, I give you advice; if you are lucky you will have seventy years of active life, and by that I mean from the age of twenty to the age of ninety; if you want to see the world never go to the same place twice.' Those were the words of Sir D'Arcy Wentworth Thompson, speaking to a Cambridge undergraduate audience in about 1930 at the age of seventy and still within his sixty-four-year tenure of the Chair of Natural History in the University of St Andrews.[1] That man of such immense erudition, both in the classics and in biology, the author of the epoch-making *'On Growth & Form'*—that seminal work of such great biological significance—largely put his own advice into practise. At any rate he had travelled very widely. And in his early travels he had been one of the first of relatively modern zoologists to visit the islands of the Bering Sea. There, and this is the point of the story, he was able to collect remnants of Steller's Seacow, already then for a century extinct. Probably few later specimens were ever collected, and British museums owe much to his vigour and enthusiasm.

1 D'Arcy Thompson (1860–1948) became Professor of Biology in University College, Dundee, in 1884, which was incorporated later into the University of St Andrews. He held the Chair of Natural History until his death.

Steller's Seacow was the largest of the recent Seacows, the very biggest of the mermaids, and they lived in Bering Sea in the North Pacific Ocean. They were discovered in 1741 and, through the depredations of seamen who ate them ruthlessly—if the expression is to be allowed—the animals became extinct in less than thirty years. Those creatures were up to thirty feet in length, harmless devourers of marine algae, very easy to catch and slaughter and most palatable to man.

I visited the Pribilof Islands myself in 1949[1] and mourned the absence of these Steller's Seacows from the region. Likewise much in mind there, too, were the Sea Otters, once so prevalent, then thought to be extinct but recently found again in tiny numbers still surviving in the Aleutian chain of islands. Once more now they begin, under careful protection, to multiply and rebuild their populations: perhaps now again there may be some few thousands in comparison with the high numbers of the past. That specifically more fortunate creature, the Alaskan Fur Seal, however, remains at the Pribilof Islands in beneficial use, the finest example in the world of the rational utilization of any stock of wild mammals. It amazes in its abundance,[2] two million animals, providing for mankind, under most careful U.S. guardianship and control, an annual toll of tens of thousands of prime skins, for the market and for the warmth and the glamour of human females. At North-East Point on St Paul Island, looking out over the massed breeding herds of fur seals, it is said that one encompasses with

1 The work was with the U.S. Fish and Wildlife Service on certain aspects of the breeding biology of the Fur Seals.

2 'The midsummer, or maximum seasonal, population is estimated at 1,978,000 animals; of this number, about 1,800,000, or 91 per cent, originate on the Pribilof Islands of Alaska.' See 'Pelage and Surface Topography of the Northern Fur Seal' *North American Fauna*, Number 64, by Victor B. Scheffer. U.S. Dept. of the Interior, Fish and Wildlife Service. 1961.

one sweep of the eye a greater number of large mammals than from any other point on earth. That is the contrast, at these near-by islands in Bering Sea, with Steller's Seacow exterminated for ever, existing now solely as a few old bones in museums which count themselves fortunate to possess them.

What other Sirenians do, then, still exist about the world in addition to the manatee? There is in fact alone one further kind, the dugong—sometimes called the Halicore—which I have in the past sought for almost but not quite in vain.

Twenty years ago, with iodine and apprehension, I chased a fungus infection across the skin of my left hand. It grew in concentric fairy rings until treatment overtook it at the wrist. That mortifying fungus had sprung from a careless prick on my thumb which I had myself inflicted when engaged at Aqaba in the disinterment of a dugong head. The skull is now in the British Museum (Natural History), de-greased, snowy white and properly labelled: my left thumb I still possess and use.

When Chief Fisheries Officer in then Mandatory Palestine and striving to build a wartime commercial fishery in the Gulf of Aqaba, I had enquired about the dugong. Rare individuals were sometimes sighted, it was said. One was taken accidently in a huge experimental net we set to stand upon the bottom, a net of heavy cod-line and a foot from knot to knot. It caught twelve-foot sawfish, and hammerheaded sharks and leathery turtles, deep water tuna species and this unfortunate lady dugong. She was buried in the sand for my later personal attention, which meant that I must deal with her when putrescent. Thence came that fungus on my hand.

What became quite clear was that in these days, whatever may have been the position in the past, the dugong is now very rare indeed in the Gulf of Aqaba. Further questioning and correspondence and journeying has shown me that it is now almost absent from the entire Gulf of Suez, and is rare indeed throughout the Red Sea. Never can there have been substantial numbers one supposes because of the scarcity of aquatic vegetation and of mangrove swamps in this mainly coralline area. Questions asked by me at Jidda, Port Sudan, Suakin, Massawa, Kamaran Island and Aden, all gave the same response—of lack of local knowledge of the existence of the dugong. And remember that fishermen are discerning people. Further personal questioning along the shores of the Arabian sea had a like result. There were negatives at Djibouti, Berbera, Makulla, Masira Island, Sallala, and Muscat. Enquiries too in the Persian Gulf had similar negative results.

Personal interest in the dugong, as one of the very rare tropical aquatic mammals, had grown naturally from earlier interest and research upon the Antarctic Seals, Weddell, Crab-eater and Leopard, to say nothing of passing acquaintance with the Elephant Seal, the greatest of the Phocids. Work on the Alaskan Fur Seal, in its fantastic herd at the Pribilof Islands in Bering Sea, came after my own brief encounter with the dugong at Aqaba. These events were a natural prelude to the desire to see, study and attempt to help the manatees, the mermaids in the mud, the tropical Atlantic representatives of the Sirenidae, whose book this is.

Regard then these Sirenians as a zoological family, considering first their form and their relationships, and then the distribution and habits of their modern representatives.

Many land mammals, of several families, have in the course of their evolution turned again to a life in or near the water, and the degree of their new adaptation varies greatly. Water rats swim enough to gain their food from aquatic vegetation but are little adapted in detailed anatomy to aquatic life. Beavers cut logs on land and build their castles in the water:

their tails are greatly flattened horizontally. Ordinary otters are adapted to the catching of fish beneath the surface of fresh-waters, and have expanded feet and somewhat broadened tails, but much of their life still is spent on land. Sea Otters, very furry, are more maritime in habit and rest merely on the rocks and breed there. They are remarkable for the purple hue of their bones. That purple is derived from the sea urchins which they eat in such abundance, sea urchins which the Otters crack upon their chests with stones as they float on their backs at the surface having risen from their food-seeking dives to the bottom. The seals, about thirty species of them, are more aquatic still, usually insulated with thick layers of blubber though yet retaining hair; their limbs have become flippers; and their external ears are gone or nearly so. Though some, like the Weddell Seal, may spend months swimming and feeding in utter darkness beneath the ice of the antarctic littoral, all still must pup on land or on the ice, and suckle 'terrestrially'. On the other hand the Cetaceans—near a hundred species of dolphins, porpoises and whales—are still more aquatically adapted. The whole life is lived in water, birth and suckling included. They have many remarkable detailed anatomical and physiological adaptations to their free pelagic life, many of them for ever roaming the open oceans. The hind limbs have vanished completely and propulsion is entirely by the hugely expanded horizontal tail: the blubber is thick and all hair has gone.

If you like so to speak or so to regard them, the Sirenians, our mermaids, lie midway in aquatic adaptation between the seals and the whales. The Sirenians have almost completely lost their hair but the blubber layer is relatively thin in those which live in tropic waters. They have also lost their hind limbs and the tail is broad and strongly propulsive. They breed, calve and suckle in the water and are incapable of emergence on to land. But still they sometimes have interest in the land, and can heave themselves up enough to put the forward part of the body on to the river bank and there eat chosen succulent vegetation. These Sirenians are riverine, estuarine and coastal living animals, not creatures of the open seas. In such marked distinction to the wholly carnivorous seals and whales, the Seacows are totally vegetarian, and their teeth show remarkable modifications and adaptations in relation to that fact.

A curious feature of manatees, indeed of dugongs too, is their mode of tooth replacement. Most of us mammals, men and maidens alike, proceed in youth with so-called milk teeth, which later are shed by the growth of the adult teeth, one permanent tooth replacing each milk tooth by growth beneath its roots. That we may call the normal mammalian arrangement. This natural process, for a variety of dietary reasons, is often inadequate in ourselves, and must be supplemented by the provision of dead porcelain artifacts attached to plastic plates. Not so the manatees and dugongs—and in this they parallel their closest zoological congeners, the elephants—the manatees and dugongs replace their teeth by a forward longitudinal movement in the jaws. The permanent teeth, with us the so-called second set, are limited to molars, that is to say grinding teeth. No incisors or canines are present in these creatures save upper second incisors in some dugongs, teeth which parallel those second incisors of elephants which, from their large size, we call tusks. The molars form, in each half jaw, a set of six to eight grinders functional in a row contemporaneously in manatees, while in dugongs it is usually only four, and in elephants fewer still. The forward teeth in each row, it will be seen on close examination, are worn relatively smooth while those behind are ridged and sharp, in fact are actually and functionally younger. Throughout these creatures' chewing adult life the teeth are worn by attrition, and as they wear the whole set moves forward. The older teeth successively reach the front position in the jaw and then are lost, while others successively emerge behind, new and strongly ridged, and in their turn suffer attrition and forward motion. So may a score or more of teeth move forward in succession along each side, both above and below. That is the number in manatees; in dugongs it is a good deal less; and in elephants again fewer still. That is the way in which the demands of constant wear are met, by the provision of more teeth in series from behind rather than, as in rodents, ruminants, and others, by perpetual growth of the individual tooth within its own stable socket. The peak of aggrandizement in that line of course is the narwhal tusk, which can achieve a length of even ten feet or more.

In contrast, Steller's Seacow had lost all its teeth in adult life and crushed the food solely by means of horny plates which presumably regrew as fast as worn away. The extent of wear of the teeth of Sirenians is perhaps surprising considering the softness of the vegetation upon which they feed. Probably the rapid wear derives from sand grains admixed with the enormous volumes of weed consumed.

There are other interesting features observable in the bones and skeletons of Sirenians. Particularly is there a regular hardening and increase of density of certain of the bones (termed pachyostosis), to produce almost the appearance of ivory. This phenomenon occurs least in dugongs and most in Steller's Seacows. It may be useful in increasing the density of the whole body, a convenience perhaps for their special mode of life. The same phenomenon is found in fossil Sirenia, while in most modern animals, including ourselves, it is counted as a rare disease called hyperostosis.

Though the total number of vertebrae in mammals may be

quite varied according to the species, there is a general insistence—so it seems—that in the neck there shall always be just seven cervical vertebrae. The exceptions to this rule are rare and among them are the Sirenians, where the cervical vertebrae regularly are six in number. The other exceptional animals are the sloths of South America where, if you take the number of toes in the name and multiply by three, you will find the number of neck vertebrae. The two-toed sloth, *Choloepus didactylus*, has six cervicals and the three-toed sloth, *Bradypus tridactylus*, has nine (or even ten).

The fossil record shows that the Seacows are not so very ancient in their evolution, the oldest known to us being *Eosiren* from the Upper Eocene of Egypt, a period of the order of fifty million years ago. Fossil Sirenians are not rare and are widely scattered over the world. Especially are there remains of Sirenians much resembling the modern dugong— remains found in Egypt, Europe (Italy, Austria, Germany, France, Belgium and England), the West Indies and California. At an earlier stage these dugongs must have inhabited most warm coasts of all the continents, whereas now they are confined to the Indo–Pacific region. The direct progenitors of the modern manatees are however as yet unknown. Even their modern Atlantic habitat has so far produced no more than fossil dugongs which in fact today are quite absent from that region.

We may summarise the modern mermaids thus: in recent times there have been three genera of Sirenians, namely the recently extinct Steller's Seacow of Bering Sea; the Indo-Pacific dugong (sometimes called Halicore); and the three species of manatee[1] in the Atlantic region. By a little to extend the detail we arrive at this arrangement:

1 *Lamantin* in French; *Peixe-Boi* (fish-ox) in Brazilian; *Seekuh* (seacow) in German.

A. DUGONGIDAE. (Dugongs)
  —*Dugong dugon* (Australia). Red Sea, coasts of East
     Africa, islands of Indian Ocean, Ceylon, Malayan
     Archipelago, Philippines and northern Australia.

B. TRICHECHIDAE. (Manatees)
  —*Trichechus senegalensis*. West African rivers and
     coastal lagoons from Senegal to Angola.
  —*Trichechus inunguis*. Amazon and Orinoco rivers.
  —*Trichechus manatus*
     Two sub-species
  —*Trichechus m. manatus*. West Indies, coasts of
     Yucatan, Southern Mexico, Central America, and
     northern South America to the Guianas.
  —*Trichechus m. latisrostris*. Florida peninsula.

C. HYDRODAMALIDAE. (Steller's Seacow)
  —*Hydrodamalis* (*Rhytina*) *Stelleri*. Bering and Copper
     Islands in Bering Sea.

Now first consider Steller's Seacow. It was a most remarkable animal and all the more sad that it was so soon exterminated by hungry seamen after its discovery by Russians in
1741. The animal grew up to a length of even thirty feet, was
slow moving, and not afraid of its new and ruthless predator.
It was the largest herbivorous aquatic mammal there has ever
been—so far as we know. It lived exclusively on marine algae,
and its mouth was armoured with no more than horny plates
with which it chumped the seaweed sufficiently for swallowing.
Of its detailed life history and habits our chief knowledge is
derived from the care and skill of the earliest observations.
And that is a tribute to Georg Wilhelm Steller. This German
naturalist was the ship's doctor with the Danish Commodore

Vitus Bering when his Russian expedition[1] was exploring the Bering Sea—so suitably named after him. In 1741 the expedition was wrecked and forced to winter at the newly-found islands named after Bering's title. Steller must have been a remarkable man to have persisted so diligently with his detailed observations despite scurvy and shipwreck in this climatically most inhospitable situation. Steller's Seacow and Steller's Eider and Steller's Sea Lion are his memorials: though the Seacow now has gone, both Steller's Eider and his Sea Lion remain to grace the region.

At this period there were many Russian exploratory voyages in the far north Pacific Ocean. Bering and Pribilof were two expedition commanders whose names remain upon the modern map, and with them and their newly-discovered islands are associated the discovery of the breeding congregations of the Seacows and the Fur Seals. The Russian geographical discoveries were soon followed by organized hunting expeditions and then by missionaries of the Russian Orthodox church. These last worked among the Aleuts of the island chain and the Indians of mainland Alaska. Despite the sale of Alaska to the United States, for seven million dollars in 1876, and all that has happened since, still the onion-domed Russian Orthodox churches may be seen in the region and indeed much further south along the American Pacific seaboard.

Steller's Seacow perhaps never was very numerous—perhaps no more than a total of 2,000 individuals at the time of their discovery. It thus resembled the extinct Dodo, that huge ground-pigeon of Mauritius, rather than the myriads of the more recently extinguished Passenger Pigeon of the United States, and the similarly now lost Great Auk of both sides of the

1 A convenient summary is available in 'Bering's Last Voyage' by Frank Debenham. Polar Record, Vol. 3, No. 22, July 1941.

North Atlantic Ocean. The Seacow lived its quiet life in Bering Sea, north of the Aleutian chain of islands, south of Bering Strait itself and centred on the Commodore Islands—Bering Island and Copper Island. There, Seacows were the aquatic vegetarian equivalents of the millions of Alaskan Fur Seals of the Pribilof Islands, feeding on fish and squids, and the numerous Sea Otters feeding largely on sea urchins and other bottom fauna. Such islands are girt about with immense tangled masses of brown algae—seaweeds bigger than our own European *Laminaria* but not competing in size with the enormous *Macrocystis* of the Southern Ocean which may extend for over three hundred feet in length. Those enormous brown algae may indeed achieve a length exceeding the height of the very tallest trees, the redwoods, the Douglas fir and certain eucalypts. The tangled heaving masses of algae are on the whole avoided by the Fur Seals who speed for food to greater distances from land, and in the non-breeding season spread on migration over the whole of the north Pacific Ocean. Those same masses of brown seaweed are the happy hunting ground of the Sea Otters who sought their food among and below them. On the other hand the Seacows ate, it seems, smaller species of green and brown algae in shallow water, and throve on them until man, the overwhelming hunter, came and slaughtered and extinguished the species for ever.

Oddly enough on a calm day and from an eminence, those huge beds of brownish seaweed in the Bering Sea, with their shining trailing ends awash at the surface yet disturbed by passing winds, bear an unexpected resemblance to fields of corn at home in England—when breezes ripple across the purpling awns of the barley fields in June. The barley must be reaped and threshed and brewed to beer or fed to our domestic stock. The Seacows browsed direct on the alga fields, contentedly we may imagine, well insulated by blubber from the chill waters and heedless of the fog which is the almost year-long attribute in chief of the centre of the Bering Sea.

Today, it must be true to say, there are no considerable aggregations of large mammals anywhere on earth which have not yet suffered a deliberate hunting effort. The only possible exceptions to that statement may be species of pelagic porpoises out in the open oceans, still preserved by their own swiftness and the difficulty of prognostication of their whereabouts. Steller's Seacows, so large, so unfearful of man, so densely congregated, were quickly exterminated. The usual estimate is twenty-seven years from discovery by predatory man.

Stejneger, Steller's biographer, referring to the period 1743 to 1763, said[1] 'hardly a winter passed without one or more parties spending eight or nine months in hunting fur-animals there' (Bering Island) 'during which time the crews lived almost exclusively on the meat of the sea-cows. But that is not all, for more than half of the expeditions which wintered there did so for the express purpose of laying in stores of sea-cow meat for their further journey, which usually lasted two to three years more. . . . From 1763 the visits to Bering Island seem to grow scarcer . . . probably due to the very fact that sea-cows had now become so nearly exterminated that the few left were insufficient to maintain any wintering and foraging expedition'. Possibly a few survived into the following century.

According to Kuntze (1932),[2] the Russian naturalist Dybowski in 1879–85 collected reports and skeletal remains

1 Quoted by Glover M. Allen in his '*Extinct and Vanishing Mammals of the Western Hemisphere*', 1942. Special Publication No. 11 of the American Committee for International Wild Life Protection.

2 See Glover M. Allen, ibid.

at Bering Island; he was told by the natives there that 'the great sea-cow still survived at the time of the arrival of the permanent settlers', which would extend the period of its existence to about 1830.[1] He mentions also, as a contributory factor to its extinction, the formation of ice along the coast from time to time, thus restricting still further its available territory.

Steller's Seacows were altogether too easy to catch. Apparently they lived in herds and fed in shallow water, coming in with the tide into areas of growing littoral algae. There they pressed so far into the shallows that often the backs of the animals were exposed and gulls perched upon them and fed on the crustacean parasites and other fauna of their rugose skins. The skin was in fact of a remarkable form, remarkable in thickness, anatomical detail and rugosity. Pieces are still available in some museums. Comparison in the early days was made with the bark of a tree, and the animal was sometimes referred to in German as 'Borkentier'—the bark animal. In free translation a passage by Steller[2] may be rendered thus in description of the surface parasites. 'The Seacow is constantly assailed by a particular crustacean like a louse. These are wont to occupy, in great numbers, usually the breasts, the nipples, the sexual orifice, the rump, and to

1 Flower and Lydekker 1891 in a footnote on p. 221 of their book *Mammals Living and Extinct* say that Nordenskiöld, during his voyage in the Vega, obtained some information from the natives of Bering Island which led him to believe that a few individuals may have survived to a much later date, even to 1854; but this conclusion is disputed by later writers.

2 All quotations from Steller in this chapter are translations from a short modern and convenient German work by Dr Erna Moh entitled *Sirenen oder Seekühe*, published in 1957 (Die neue Brehm Bücherei. A. Ziemsen Verlag. Wittenberg Lutherstadt). The author is indebted to the British Museum (Natural History) for the loan of a translation by Cmdr. J. M. Chaplin, R.N. (ret'd).

habit the hard pits in the cuticle. Since the crustaceans eat
rough the cuticle and skin there are formed warts here and
ere from the exuded tissues below. These attract seagulls
nich sit on the animals' backs and seek with their sharp beaks
is agreeable food and thus render a friendly and pleasant
rvice to the tormented animals.' The crustaceans are in fact
amus rhytina, an Amphipod, which shares the host with
rtain barnacles.

The extreme thickness and rugosity of the hide was
esumably an adaptation to the dangers of mechanical
rasion by ice floes under the influence of heavy surf in the
allow waters where the animals fed.

Killing beasts so large, so docile and so palatable was all too
sy. The unfortunate creatures were, it seems, simply im-
led upon great hooks by men coming among them in boats in
e shallow water. Then they were dragged ashore by ropes,
ruggling and groaning and spouting blood from their many
ounds. Struggling still they were lanced, speared and cut
out with knives until at last their lives departed. Sometimes
seems that when a female was killed the attendant male, or
veral males, would even further increase their own danger by
lowing her unto the water's edge, and then remaining even
the vicinity of the carcase on the beach. This same occurrence
s been noted too in accounts of hunting the manatees of the
nazon in Brazil. There, too, if a female first could be
oked or roped the males would assemble and hazard them-
lves—nobly, unwittingly, automatically as you may like to
terpret—to the gratification of the hunters and the depletion
the stock.

To get the harpooned animals to the shore a rope party of
irty was required, so Steller tells us, who 'held the beast and,
ainst a fearful resistance by it, dragged it ashore by a great
ort. Those however who were in the boat made themselves

fast to another rope and exhausted the animal with constant
blows and strokes so much that finally it became motionless
and tired and they killed it with pikes, knives and other
weapons and pulled it ashore. Some cut quite big pieces out of
the still living animal. All that the animal did meanwhile was
to thrash about mightily with its tail and so resisted with its
forearms that frequently large pieces of the outer skin burst
off. In addition it took very heavy breaths groaning therewith.
From the wounded back the blood spurted like a fountain. As
long as its head remained below water no blood flowed. As
soon however as it lifted its head clear and drew breath the
blood shot out again. . . .'

Steller went on to remark: 'Old and very large beasts are
more easily taken than the calves because the calves move
much more powerfully and . . . when the skin is burst they tear
themselves free. If the beast, after being caught with the hook
begins to move more violently then not only the adjacent ones
of the herd moved and are provoked to come to the aid of the
captive. Some seek to capsize the boat with their backs, others
lie upon the rope and endeavour to break it or try by beating
with the tail to get the hook out of the wounded animal's back
which at times they have tried with good results. A very
remarkable proof of their love for kin and mate is that the male
shoots like an arrow quite without hope after the female who is
already dead, having tried with all his might but vainly to free
her from the hook that is dragging her, and having thus
received many blows from us nevertheless followed her to the
beach. When next day early we returned to cut up the meat
and take it home we found the male again with his female and
even on the third day I have seen him when I went along alone
to examine the intestines.'

'These beasts like shallow and sandy places on the sea shore
but above all they love to dwell at the mouths of small rivers t

which the sweetness of the debouching water entices them at all times in crowds. The young animals and pups, when they go to their pasture, are allowed to precede them but they hem them in from behind and at the sides very carefully and always keep them in the middle of the herd. With the flood tide they approach so near to the beach that I was able to reach them not only with a stick or lance but have also stroked their backs with my hands at times. If they are rather badly injured they do nothing except to retreat further from the shore but after a short while they forget about it and return. Commonly whole families live together, the male with the female a grown-up and a quite young animal. Seemingly they pair off. They give birth at all seasons but usually in autumn as I assumed by the pups born at that time. As however they mostly mate at the beginning of spring I concluded that their period of gestation is over a year. That they produce only one pup is concluded from the shortness of the teats and the number of the breasts. I have also never seen more than one calf round its mother'.

'These voracious animals feed without pause and from great greed keep their heads continually underwater without bothering about their lives or safety. So a man in a boat quite naked can go right amongst them and choose one of the herd with assurance and throw his hook. Their entire toil whilst feeding is that every four or five minutes they poke their noses out of the water and blow out air, as well as a little water, with a noise similar to the snorting of a horse. During feeding they move one foot after the other slowly forward so that they are partly swimming slowly and partly pacing along as cattle and sheep do when grazing. Half the body, namely the back and sides, are at all times raised out of the water. Whilst they are eating the gulls alight upon their backs and feed on the lice infesting the skin; just as the crows with the lice of pigs and sheep. They do not however eat all brown algae indiscriminately. . . . Wherever they have stayed for a day immense heaps of roots and stems are cast on the beach by the waves. When their bellies are filled some sleep lying on their backs. They retreat from the beach so that they shall not be left lying high and dry when the tide goes out. In winter they are frequently suffocated by ice which floats into the shore and are cast upon the shore dead; which also happens if they get into the surf, which beats upon the rocks with violence, and are thereby also flung against the rocks. In winter they are so thin that one can see their backbone as well as all their ribs. In the spring they mate like human beings and especially towards the evening, if the sea is calm. Before they come together many love-games take place. The female swims slowly to and fro the male following. He deceives the female by many twists and turns and devious courses until finally she herself becomes bored and gets tired and forced to lie on her back, whereupon the male comes raging towards her to satisfy his ardour and both embrace each other'.

'As regards the voice, the animal is dumb, and does not utter a sound; it breathes very heavily and sighs and groans only when it has been wounded. Whether it has good eyes and ears I cannot say'.

'The fat which surrounds the whole body is . . . dense, shiny, white and when laid in the sun yellow as spring butter. It smells and tastes very pleasantly and . . . even to be preferred to the fat of the quadrupeds by far. For not only can it be kept in the hottest weather for very long but also does not become rancid or smelly. When it is cooked it tastes very sweet and good so that it took away all our appetites for butter. In taste it almost approaches that of the oil of sweet almonds and can be used . . . just like butter. In a lamp it burns brightly without smoke or smell. Perhaps it will not be without use in medicines because it is a mild laxative and if drunk in considerable quantity at once, does not cause any disgust and does not spoil the appetite. Perhaps it will be more useful to those suffering from the pains of stone than the mastication of bones or so-called manatu stones. The tail fat is denser and harder and when cooked better tasting. The flesh has to a certain extent stronger and thicker fibres than beef. It is redder than that of land animals'.

'The meat is, when cooked, even though it takes rather long to cook, of very good taste and not easily distinguished from beef. The fat of the calves is so similar to fresh pork fat that it can hardly be distinguished from it. The flesh is however just like veal. It can be easily cooked to tenderness and swells during cooking so that it takes up twice as much room in the pot as before. . . . The intestines, the heart, the liver, the kidneys are much too tough and we did not hanker after them as we had meat in abundance.'

All those paragraphs are from Steller's original description and very lucid they are. Steller's biographer was the zoologist Stejneger who pointed out, in 1887[1] 'there can hardly be any doubt that these animals were the last survivors of a once more numerous and more widely distributed species, which had been spared to that late date because man had not yet reached their last resort. It is, then, pretty safe to assume that this colony was not on the increase and that, under the most favourable circumstances, the number of surviving young ones barely balanced the number of deaths caused by the dangers of the long winters. Under this supposition, every animal killed by a new agency—in this case by man—represents one less in the total number'. Slow and stationary in habit, unsuspicious, and without means of defence or escape, its disappearance,

1 See 'How the Great Northern Sea-Cow (Rytina) was Extermi-nated' by Leonhard Stejneger. *The American Naturalist*, December 1887, Vol. XXI, No. 12.

Stejneger asserts, 'was simply due to man's greed'. Brandt (1846) in his monograph writes: 'Stupiditas animalis summa fuit.'

Steller's Seacows were the only Sirenians available in large and all too easily visible aggregations, and they suffered accordingly: the hunting was far too simple for the species' good. So they were soon extinguished for ever. The dugongs and the manatees, certainly it seems, are somewhat gregarious, but the modern depletion of their numbers gives us now no chance to observe the original extent of the aggregations. It is probable however that such aggregations, as did exist, were rarely comparable in size with those of Steller's Seacows. But there is one record, at least, of an enormous herd of dugongs yet without true indication of the actual number. Glover Allen may be quoted. He writes: 'In his excellent account of the dugong, Troughton (1928, 1932) says that in 1893 large herds were a common sight in Moreton Bay, Brisbane, and that fishing or netting was carried out there and at Hervey Bay, but the slow breeding of the animals has usually put a stop to ungoverned slaughter. They are not so plentiful now between Brisbane and Cairns, eastern Queensland, and range round the north coast of Australia to Broome on the west coast. In July, 1893, a herd in Moreton Bay was reported as extending over a length of about three miles with a width of 300 yards.'

The secretive, surreptitious, private way of life of these lesser and surviving Seacows must always have made accurate observation difficult. That habit has doubtless been their saving grace, their protective and most fortunate reaction. It has saved them until this day but the danger presses all about them for men are terribly ingenious in their modes of hunting.

Men set nets on the bottom to entangle the dugongs, or

they fasten loops with pegs to the bottom to noose and drown the manatees in the rivers. Men can come silently in dugout canoes, waiting and watching, then use spear and lance, with attached ropes and bladders and wooden floats. Men can wound the nostril valves with shot knowing that then the desperate creatures must surface repeatedly or drown. Men can learn that, in the Amazon, manatees may lurk in groups beneath drifting islands of floating vegetation, breathing through gaps in the centre. There the hunter may station himself with devastating effect upon those which lurk unsuspecting below but must needs rise for air at intervals. Men may take the female resting after copulation, even use her— then in season—to attract males to their death as well.

In contrast with Steller's Seacow and its extremely restricted distribution in the cold Bering Sea, the dugong is today still widely spread in the warm waters of the western Pacific and Indian Oceans. Its modern range extends from Queensland and northern Australia to the Philippine Islands, from the Malay Archipelago to the islands of the Bay of Bengal and Ceylon, and from the east coast of Africa to Arabia and the Red Sea.

Compared with the three existing species of the manatee, and fairly acceptable subspecies as well, the dugong is in general now regarded as all belonging to a single widespread species. The dugong grows in fact to a length of about ten feet but the measurements available are few. Compared with the manatee with its rounded, rather shovel-like tail, the dugong's tail is broadly notched in the middle line and has pointed lateral lobes, though in that last respect not to the extent in Steller's Seacow whose tail was approximating to the shape in many whales. Otherwise the dugong and the manatee outwardly are not so very different from one another to the non-zoological observer. However the dugong is in general lighter in colour beneath and its hairs are more numerous.

Everywhere however it seems, the dugongs are now becoming much diminished in numbers as a result of excessive pressures from mankind. Wherever they occur fishermen find them easy and acceptable prey. My own dugong, already mentioned, was one of the last survivors from the extreme north-westward point of the creature's geographical range, in the Gulf of Aqaba. My own further enquiries in the Red Sea and along the Arabian coasts demonstrated the creatures' modern rarity in that region. Erna Mohr[1] has collected evidence from elsewhere and the story is the same.

It appears that in about 1930 a yearly catch of about sixty dugongs was still being taken at Kilakaria, a seaport on the Indian side of the Gulf of Manaar. They were also said to occur then near the north and north-western coasts of Ceylon but to be diminishing in numbers. Round Madagascar, too, Mohr says there have been rapid decreases in abundance over the last two or three decades.

Glover Allen[2] quotes records such as these: 'said to have been "apparently plentiful" at Kosseir in the Red Sea in 1870', but by 1932 they were, according to Major Flower 'now rare on the (Red Sea) coast of Egypt'; 'rarely north of lat. 25°N., but not uncommon to the south'; in 1932 De Beaux said dugongs were 'captured near Assab' on the coast of Eritrea, 'more frequently than elsewhere'; 'in 1929' Phillips implied that they were no longer to be found in any numbers in the Gulf of Manaar' and obviously were diminishing off the coasts of Ceylon. They had at one time been regularly sent by train to the market in Colombo. Glover Allen also states that at one time dugongs were to be found in small numbers in the Straits of Malacca, off the Siamese coast, Sumatra and

1 loc. cit.
2 loc. cit.

Borneo, and north to the Philippine Islands and then, in the Japanese current, even north to Formosa.

More recent information from the Red Sea is summarised in a later valuable paper by Gohar,[1] the Director of the Marine Biological Station at Al Ghardaqa at the entrance to the Gulf of Suez. In particular he lists data from sixteen specimens deliberately taken by net in the course of thirteen years after previously believing the animal to be extinct in the area. Gohar provides some interesting photographs of dugongs and explains the way in which the animals seem to use the flippers in the shallow waters of lagoons, to dig out the sea grass (*Diplanthera uninervis*) which in that region is the exclusive food of the dugong. Gohar, from his studies, would confirm earlier proposals for subspecific distinction for the Red Sea form as *Dugong dugong tabernaculi*. There is no doubt however that the Red Sea dugong is now an animal of rarity.

Gohar interestingly refers to the mermaid legend which he would firmly attribute, if at all, to the dugong and not the manatee. He may be quoted thus:

'In the dugong, the oval face of the relatively small head, of light colour and roughly the same size as a human face, also the fatty chin and the protruding nose-like alveolus of the upper jaw, lying over a small mouth, all these are characters that enhanced the resemblance to a human face. The flat ventral surface of the muzzle gives the impression of a woman hanging a veil over her head to below the eyes.

'It has also been claimed that the mother has been seen, in shallow water, holding her large-size young with one or both flippers and standing waist-high out of the water, while

1 H. A. F. Gohar, '*The Red Sea Dugong*'. Publications of the Marine Biological Station Al Ghardaqa (Red Sea) No. 9. 1957. I myself worked at this fascinating station in 1933–4, but neither saw nor heard of dugongs then.

suckling the young at its well-developed pectoral breasts. At all events, it is imperative that the mother should, during suckling, maintain her own as well as her offspring's nostrils above the water for aerial respiration. The resemblance to a woman carrying her child has been accentuated by the great shyness of dugongs, which made it impossible to watch them except at a great distance, and often only in the darker nights. At the sight of an approaching object or person, they dived and the appearance of the tail beating the surface of the water aroused the curiosity and served to enliven and perpetuate the sea-man's faith in such mythical creatures.'

'The stories of mermaids were especially told by voyagers in the south-eastern seas, where only dugongs occurred. Furthermore, it is of special interest to remember, in this connection, the many stories told of marriages taking place between mermaids and men. Marriages which—the stories often went on to relate—resulted in an offspring that talked the languages of both the father and the mother etc. Although such stories are extremely imaginative, yet they cannot be passed over without some meditation, as they must have some meaning which may lead us to the clue of the problem we are confronted with. At the same time, due consideration should be given to the following facts: 1) The great resemblance between the genitalia of dugongs and those of man; 2) That dugongs are warm-blooded animals and, on account of their blubber, will retain the high temperature of their bodies for some hours after death, especially in the hot climate of the regions in which they occur; 3) That they are docile and inoffensive creatures; 4) That in old times voyages took very long and men were for months and even years, away from their homes and families, at sea or in places or islands completely devoid of human inhabitants. Considering these facts together, it is not difficult to understand, under such abnormal conditions, how much femininity a thing like a female dugong may suggest and how much the seizure or even the sight of one may mean. It may be remembered that, in this respect, man has not completely raised himself above the rank of animals.'

Straightforward consumption of the flesh was doubtless the primary reason for the taking of dugongs, but Glover Allen tells us that there were special features too. 'While the dugong seems to be mainly prized for its flesh, which is said to resemble pork or bacon . . . and for its oil, hide, and even tusks, we learn from an old work published in 1665, concerning the famous mission of de Goyer and de Keyser from Batavia to Canton and Peking, that the Chinese held in high esteem certain stones found in the heads of these seacows, which they say have the property of clearing the kidneys of every kind of sand and gravel and of removing obstructions from the lower parts afflicted by them. These "stones" were very likely the dense tympanic bones of the dugong. Sowerby, in discussing this matter, states that so far as known to him there is no record in Chinese literature of the dugong's occurrence in the coastal waters of that country.'

There is also reference to supposed aphrodisiac properties of items from the dugong. That is in line with the still existing trade in spurious aphrodisiacs which extends from the dried testicles of Sea Lions and Fur Seals to the horns of the remaining rhinoceroses of Africa.

Erna Mohr[1] has collected other interesting details a few of which may be quoted here in free translation. A dugong of about a quarter of a ton weight yields perhaps a dozen gallons of oil. Its taste is not unpleasant, and it is odourless. Beneath the oil-bearing blubber lies a layer of white fat which is very similar to pork fat. The fishermen of Ceylon regard the oil as an

[1] loc. cit.

obstetric remedy, also use it for cooking. The natives of the coastal regions of north-western Australia ascribe great medicinal potency to the oil. The inhabitants of the Comoro Islands treat boils with dugong bone meal, while people in Madagascar use it for pulmonary diseases. Fat from the head is used for headaches and earaches whilst the body fat mixed with rice serves as a cathartic and is used for leprosy and skin diseases. Roast dugong meat is said to be indistinguishable from well-flavoured but somewhat tough beef. It is remarkable that like the flesh of the manatee it remains eatable even in the heat of its native climate for at least three days. (Steller too remarked upon the long lasting quality of his beasts' meat and put forward an hypothesis in explanation.) It is reported that in the thinly inhabited and rather primitive regions of north-west Australia dugong meat and turtle eggs serve for the bacon and eggs of the breakfast table. The Mohammedans of Ceylon and the Indian coasts value dugong meat highly, while some of the people of Madagascar observe special rites when preparing the flesh for eating. The butchering must be carried out secretly and silence must be kept. The animal must be covered by cloths and not observed while being carved. There must be rites too to ensure that future catches will not diminish —unsuccessful rites, sadly it must be pointed out. Dugong bones and skins are employed on a modest scale. The skins are tanned for leather.

Mohr concludes her descriptions and comments upon the dugong with information that northwards of Broome on the north-west coast of Australia dugongs still graze in herds.[1] Let us hope that will long remain true: it is a region of pearl fishing so that human predators can by no means be absent. Yet that perhaps is the most promising place left on earth

1 There is protective Australian legislation said to limit the killing of dugongs to 'natives'.

to which to travel to study the species in any detail and abundance.

An older source,[1] at the end of the last century, stated that the dugong of Australia 'has lately been the object of a regular "fishery", chiefly on account of its oil, which is peculiarly clear, limpid, and free from disagreeable smell, and is said to have the same medicinal properties as cod-liver oil. Although often stated in books to attain the length of twenty feet when adult, there does not appear to be any evidence from actual specimens in museums that dugongs ever reach half that size, eight feet being the common length of adult animals.'

Efforts are being made by correspondence to acquire a wide picture of the present distribution and abundance—more truly scarcity—of the dugongs, but inevitably the information will be incomplete and in general discouraging. The prospects for the long-continued existence of the species must be judged to be poor in these days of ever-increasing human predatory effort.

An interesting recent record[2] refers to a population of dugongs in Manda Bay, on the coast of Kenya. There is good government control of their well-being and they are not now hunted deliberately as formerly they were with spears at night. Local fishermen claim their numbers have not diminished in living memory, and that at certain seasons a herd of even 120 may be seen. These animals spend the day beyond the reef and come inshore feeding in shallower water at night.

The investigator Rüppel attempted to show (so Mohr tells us) that the ark of the covenant which the ancient Israelites

1 *An Introduction to the Study of Mammals living and extinct* by W. H. Flower and R. Lydekker. 1891.

2 This information comes verbally from P. J. Jarman, a zoologist with the Second Oxford Expedition to the Kiunga Archipelago. 1961.

carried in their wanderings was covered with untanned dry dugong leather for which reason he coined the (now redundant) name for the dugong of the Red Sea, *Halicore tabernaculi.*

Whether or not in fact the ark of the covenant was covered with dugong skin several millennia ago, it is certain that up to the middle nineteen-forties there was a substantial export of manatee hides from Brazil. Manaos was the centre of the trade; hides and cooked meat packed in cans in its own fat were the products; and *Trichechus inunguis* were the victims. The records are available in a Brazilian publication[1] which is of much interest. More recent details have so far been impossible to obtain, or perhaps one should say that the real efforts made have so far yielded no success. Perhaps, and probably, that is because the manatees now have been so reduced in numbers that they are quite incapable of supporting the trade and that there consequently are no statistics at all today to be collected. Or it may be that, despite telstar and all the modern devices to increase and expedite human communication from land to land, ultimately, worthwhile and detailed communication depends upon the will to communicate after a request has been received.

Here however are a few details from that publication of 1945. The skins as despatched weighed on average something over twenty kilograms each. The totals seemingly passing through the hands of one firm in Manaos were: in 1938 669 skins; in 1939 1064; in 1940 2,370; in 1941 435; in the first half of 1942 1,011 skins. The destinations of the skins given in another table included Pernambuco, Rio de Janeiro and Lisbon. Those were the skins of *Trichechus inunguis* of the Amazon, a purely freshwater species confined to that river and many of its innumerable tributaries, and the Orinoco as

1 Nunes Pereira, loc. cit.

well. This species is characterized by the absence of nails on the flippers, which are proportionately elongated, and a white breast patch. Glover Allen[1] gives some account of the past experience of the species and its hunting for its excellent sweet meat, and for its hide. Brigantines were at one time regularly sent from Cayenne with salt to do business in Amazon waters with the hunters who provided great quantities of manatee meat in exchange for 'beads, knives, white hats of a low price, some linen, toys and iron tools'. Guiana manatees probably suffered similar depredations in the seventeenth century.[2]

Glover Allen, writing in 1942, concluded in effect that the creature was now, by hard hunting, diminishing in abundance in the main river and the larger affluents. The extent to which this process has continued in the last twenty years into the upper waters is not known for certain. But the effectiveness of Brazilian hunters has undoubtedly, and sadly for the manatees, been greatly increased in recent years with the rapid spread of both rifles and power boats, and that most certainly in the presence of strong demand for their produce.

Our mermaids in the mud of the Guianas—*Trichechus manatus manatus*, the West Indian manatee—has still very much to be learnt about it, as we have seen. Its original distribution over the north-east coast and rivers of South America, around many of the islands of the Caribbean, and along the coasts of Yucatan and southern Mexico, Panama and Nicaragua, is well attested. Its present, residual distribution and numbers is little known indeed. Glover Allen, again, gives some fascinating past details but the picture is certainly of a species in rapid retreat—and that is a polite euphemism for

1 loc. cit.

2 C. de Jong states that in the seventeenth century manatees were abundant in Guiana rivers and ships were specially chartered in Amsterdam to take meat. See *De Surinaamse Landbouw*, 9e Jaargang. 1961.

being rapidly killed under the pressure of human hunting and slaughter whenever and wherever opportunity offers. The manatee is so much a creature whose disappearance can pass unnoticed: unobtrusive even when abundant, in increasing rarity it slips away unobserved, unmourned by all except the biologists and the conservators aware of its potentialities. A species grown very rare and scarce is indubitably better than actual extinction, but scarcity precludes all actual usefulness.

In the Caribbean region as a whole the manatee must perforce be much more maritime than it is in the Guianas where great rivers are added to its living space. The general picture, on the tenuous evidence available, is that the manatee is now almost certainly rare over the whole of its former range with the exception of the mainland rivers and coasts. Its status in the Guianas has already been described: its status in Venezuela and Colombia needs much investigation both by correspondence and investigation in those lands themselves. Neither course is easy and both require time in abundance.

Glover Allen may be quoted for the supposition 'that the "three mermaids" that Columbus reported near Punta Roxa were manatees, the first record of the species in literature. In Oviedo's history there is a further account of the manatee, with which Columbus on his fourth voyage, in 1502, had then become more familiar. The translation of Herrera speaks of it as a new sort of fish, which was a considerable advantage to them and relates the story of a tame one kept by the Cacique Carametex in a pond for 26 years; "it grew tame and sensible and would come when called by the name of Mato, which signifies Noble".'

Allen also makes special note of the manatees' keen sense of hearing of which the hunters were well aware. He also says that 'In Yucatan not only is the flesh in much demand, but the hide, which may be up to four centimeters thick, is sold for a good price to be made into canes, which, varnished yellow, are much prized locally. Likewise the fisherman play upon the credulity of their fellows, who believe that the bones of the manatee possess marvellous curative properties for certain complaints so that these are therefore largely used to make charms'. Further uses of the creature's oil were as fuel for lamps in churches, as a dressing for meat, as a lubricant and for softening leather.

To Glover Allen, too, we are indebted for two biological details: 'Families consisting of a bull, a cow, and one or two immature calves, are usually met with; these groups merge into a loose herd of from ten to fifty or more individuals living in a lagoon or certain stretch of river, concentrating during the day and scattering at night.' 'Mating is said to take place in shallow water, and the single young remains with the cow until half grown. Barrett states that the average adult is eight to ten feet in length, rarely twelve feet.'

The Florida manatee is generally regarded as sub-specifically distinct, *Trichechus manatus latisrostis* but the distinguishing characters[1] are seemingly tenuous. However, passing within a very few days from extended personal observation of the captive manatees in the Botanic Gardens in Georgetown B.G. to view the captives in their pool at the Seaquarium at Miami, one did get the impression of a slightly different animal, in particular one having a longer neck and wider head, and perhaps a smaller 'face'. These are however no more than subjective judgements on a particular occasion. That the Florida manatees should be distinct from those of the remainder of the Caribbean region is unexpected, but seems to be so.

1 Joseph Curtis Moore, 'The Range of the Florida Manatee', *The Quarterly Journal* of the Florida Academy of Science, 1951. Vol. 14 No. 1.

In general, the range of the Florida manatee is the coastal waters, lagoons, and lower parts of rivers of the Florida peninsula. The furthest north record is one caught in 1919 near Wilmington N.C.[1] It is clear that the Florida peninsula in the past had many manatees though today there are few. However the residuum is now well and sensibly protected by United States legislation, which is believed to be effective—and that is far from true of much legislation in the world today designed to protect particular creatures of many species. J. C. Moore, from whom quotations have already been made in a preceding chapter, is the acknowledged authority on all things manatus in Florida.

The last of all the Seacows of the world which has not yet received attention here is the third species of manatee, the West African, *Trichechus senegalensis*. It differs little in bodily form from our creatures of the Caribbean. Its tropical African habitat is extensive geographically along the coast and up into the many rivers, even far up them. Glover M. Allen again summarized information up to 1942 and since then little has been collected and distilled into convenient form. The generalized picture is however again the same, former abundance changing into present scarcity or absence. To no one is this advantageous, to very many is this unfortunate. In large degree the seed corn has been consumed; the opportunity of a regular and useful supply of meat has gone through the rapacity of too many people.

Everywhere that is the modern picture of the Seacows of the world—they are gone or going. Without our careful aid, now protectively, they will soon all be gone for ever.

1 Glover M. Allen, loc. cit., quoting H. H. Brimley, 1931.

4

~~~~~~~~~~

Cutlass and Kiskadee

THE GUIANAS, the ancient El Dorado, hold very special attractions for the zoologist or botanist today. There is so much that is rare and strange, novel and exciting, of special comparative fascination for those knowledgeable elsewhere. It may then be appropriate to comment on varied topics which seem to be of special interest, which means of course comment upon those things, both great and small, which have in fact stimulated one's own fancy. The temporary visitor has perhaps no time to judge the whole in fully rounded proportion but he may add new perspectives by the description of extensions to his own interests. I do not refer to political commentary: that seems to be too often avidly acceptable from any newcomer anywhere despite its basis of quite inadequate evidence and width of vision. But comment may be allowable upon some of those background biological factors upon which the ephemeral political scene is played. A country composed of more than average elderly people will, for example, not be prone to revolution. Political seething, innovation and volatility are to be expected in any country whose contemporary age structure provides a preponderance of younger people. Such biological phenomena may properly be discussed by all who have at heart the happiness of other peoples. This is attempted in the next chapter.

Here now are a few pictures of Guianese life in the sense of living things, life that fascinates the observant visitor, life forms to which one must return one day for further acquaintance. We may flit from facet to facet of reality, flitting with a volatility which is itself perhaps characteristic of the gay Guianese themselves. And travel and enquiry is made so much easier and pleasanter for visitors from Britain because English is the language of the area and is the mother tongue of all B.G.'s people other than some among the Amerindians. In this very literate land, the English spoken is often so old world in its intonation, so rich in vocabulary even among those with little formal education, that contacts normally are easy with the mass of courteous and friendly people no matter what the racial background or the place in the social or occupational hierarchy—from prelate to pork-knocker[1] as one might say.

Now a virtue of the English language is the immensity of its vocabulary compared with all other languages of the globe, though that is a matter which mainly concerns the educated. Quite apart from the convenience for foreigners of the absence of inflexions, declensions and special endings—an absence which emphasizes the foreignness of foreigners on account of their ignorance of the few exceptions—two other conveniences of the tongue exist. The one is the fewness of the total words needed for communication between uneducated people and those reared in foreign lands; the other is the astonishing use made of monosyllabic words. This emphasis on the simple syllable results however in the same small word being used in different senses and, ourselves not being Chinese, without change of tone. A chop of mutton or of pork is the result of the corresponding verbal activity; a chop-suey is a Chinese

1 The pork-knocker—of which now there are fewer than some decades back—is an individualist, a free-lance gold or diamond miner, with the attributes of such people everywhere.

lish of English restaurants where a chopping process has presumably been undertaken in advance so as to save the effort of
mastication. But in the lands of Guiana a chop is an illegal but
common activity, regularly reported in the papers—'girl
chopped and robbed'—'man, choked, chopped and robbed'—
another chop in Campbellville'—and so on. In B.G. a chop
is the activity of the cutlass; pork and mutton are rare; the
chops of the old world kind are replaced in the rising lands of
new-sought affluence by that North American status symbol,
the T-bone steak whose consumption is now so widespread,
expensive and greedy. Sugar cane, your rival, your corial
paddle, are all chopped with the self-same cutlass, that alli-
gator-incised steel blade from Birmingham. Manatees too, on
occasion are chopped and that may well be their fate if introduced, for purposes of weed clearance, into channels too narrow
or too close to too many meat-loving humans.

The cutlass is indeed the workaday tool of the Caribbean
region and the alligator is the trade mark of the Birmingham
firm which makes the best of them. As the hoe and the axe
may be the tools of simple men elsewhere, in Guiana the
cutlass has a predominance which is almost absolute, shared
only in very small degree by the long handled narrow spade,
and the adze among the timber men. The cutlass can do all
things, as can its cousins, the machete of Spanish-influenced
America and the panga of East Africa. The cutlass is primitive
in the generality of its functions yet is advanced in the quality
of its substance and manufacture. Compared with old-world
lands, such as densely-populated Egypt, the Caribbean use of
the high grade imported manufactured article shows real
advance both in purchasing power and agricultural zeal. The
fellahin of Egypt have the hoe and the sickle, but the people of
the Caribbean, perhaps in debt to the early mariners and then
in connection with the plantation growth of sugar, is dependent

upon the cutlass. Its universality must amaze the visitor. The cane crop, the tops of coconuts, the clearance of waterways, and the paths through the bush, are all cut by cutlass in the hands of men and women alike. Even women weeding rose beds in the Botanic Gardens in Georgetown will do so with the aid of a cutlass.

Supposedly the cutlass derives from the maritime explorers, exploiters, traders and developers from across the Atlantic. The cutlass was never an agricultural tool in Europe; it was the seaman's all purpose weapon, offensive, defensive and otherwise functional—like the Boy Scouts knife it must be capable of anything. And so it is today.

Another example of influence from the sea, from the British Navy, is the universal playing of hockey around the coasts of Arabia and in the Persian Gulf. That is a strange contrast with the universality of cricket, the product of British inland dwellers, in the West Indies. So does an area acquire its own special glosses and characteristics which are so evident to the discerning visitor. Local speciality fortunately varies greatly, for many reasons, historical and otherwise and these happily enhance the intrinsic variety based on geography and climate and differences in fauna and flora. The people too are different, just as all people are themselves individual with an astonishing range of attributes, potentialities and yearnings. So is built and flourishes that immense range of variation which attracts the traveller whose eyes are open and who seeks not, and certainly expects not, a replica of the customs of his own land. Disappointed in the Guianas are those who expect—and from particular lands there seem to be too many such—coffee, hot dogs and miniature brass warming pans available at every stopping place and only acceptably differing by being embellished with plastic ribbon in the national colours. Neither is there a veneer of religiosity.

Fortunately the Guianas are not at all like that; they have a simplicity and a courtesy, a faunistic and floristic identity of their own. That identity, that territorial personality, can never be described in fullest detail, for it varies with the eye of the beholder. Something of the essence of the Guianas is here set down as it pleased the eyes and widened the experience of just one interested observer. Vividness, vitality and variety make the distillate of the Guianese essence. All description is inadequate but failure to attempt it is as if a plant be allowed to blossom in a closed box, its beauty unregarded. As a bee may appreciate disconnected facets of a flower bed, so one may skip and savour the details of a new land. Yet comparison is always valid.

As the cutlass is the universal tool of rural Guiana, so is the Kiskadee the ubiquitous bird of the area. '*Qu'est ce que dit,*' with variations, is the bird's perpetual exclamation, almost wherever you may travel, within the city, in the cultivated coastal plain, in the forests, along the rivers, on the savannas. There are several closely related species varying a little in size, voice and colouration, but Kiskadee in common parlance includes them all. Yellow and black admixed with white, provide the general hue for this bird which is a little bigger than an English blackbird, but more upright in its stance, and with a bigger beak. The cheerful sibilant notes of the Kiskadee are companionable and soothing and accompany one around a land of great biological and natural beauty if not often of grandeur.[1] It is hard indeed, to remember a bird, anywhere, of similar versatility and catholicity of taste in habitat. Indubitably, if British Guiana were to become a member of the

---

1 The Kiaeteur falls are regarded locally as the acme of all that can be grandest in scenic splendour. Fine indeed they are, yet so are falls elsewhere in the world, of varying and competing heights, volumes and surroundings.

International Council for Bird Preservation, and in that capacity had to choose an avian emblem, the Kiskadee should be the one. It is elegant and ubiquitous, and provides for the traveller a lasting impression of gay volubility. In comparison the robin, the chosen symbol of the United Kingdom, makes a negligible impact on the visitor, either visually or auditorily; and its relationship to the demeanour of the natives of this island kingdom is a strongly negative correlation if there is validity at all in such a concept.

One must not perhaps speak too harshly for the robin is assuredly much cherished, and is cockney-like in its vitality, pert boldness and continuous friendliness. In mighty contrast is the Bald-headed Eagle, the emblem of the great United States of America whose people have now, by a kind of hybrid vigour composed of vestigial pioneer spirit and the search for souvenirs, very nearly managed to exterminate the species completely. Were it not for that wretched and all too likely fate one might suggest the Hoatzin as Guiana's bird, though its lack of adaptability and rigidity of habitat must be recognized as the very opposite of the actual attributes of the people of Guiana.

One of our visits to the haunts of Hoatzins was in a launch which belonged to a particular Christian denomination whose main stretch of influence was riverine, along the Berbice. This launch was a rare visitor to the Canje, which is inhabited, so we were told, in its lower reaches by Seventh Day Adventists. Its upper reaches are occupied by long-established Scottish Presbyterians, who are equally smiling people of African origin. Those of another origin said both were feckless, eaters of animals rather than more nearly vegetarian like the East Indian cultivators of rice, or workers on the down-river sugar estates. The extent to which our launch captain was duty-bound in navigation was obvious, but whether denominationally bound to the Christian sect which owned the launch, was never clear. In mid-afternoon, to the detriment of good navigation among the patches of floating vegetation which on occasion blocked the whole river's course, and in the midst of theological argument, he called for the Bible from the engine room. And there, in the first verse of Isaiah Chapter 4, it is written that 'in those days seven women shall take one man'. With this happy but rather dubious relevance he was able to justify the availability of an odd plethora of brothers-in-law who so kindly provided him with a toll of bananas, pineapples and sweet corn. This, too, was the background of his so-called 'out-children', a not uncommon term in Caribbean use where life-long monogamous marriage is more rare than the strict feel proper. Terms like 'permanent concubinage' and 'accustomed woman' have their special meanings. Some are wed as children and as arranged by parents; some—of another racial origin—feel that living together may start as and when convenient but that the 'marriage' does not take place until there is money enough for an enormous party; and that may be years ahead.

In lands of varied customs based on varied racial origins, odd things most naturally occur. Thus, presumably, has come about that surprising table, in the Trinidad official statistics, entitled 'Male Maternities'. It is not that people here grow up hermaphrodite, nor regularly change their sex like that extraordinary mollusc *Crepidula fornicata* which lives in stacks of alternating males and females which, individually and conveniently, change their sex simultaneously. The male maternities of Trinidad have a simpler explanation. So careful is the registration in a land of impermanence in personal affairs, that at the registration of the birth of each new child the father states the number of his known pre-born children, just as he states his age alongside the similar details for the woman of this particular occasion. A table of paternity sounds too simple.

Official statistics, registrations and matrimonial rules provide a fund of information, not entirely divorced from amusement sometimes, for those who read. One was, for example, credibly informed, in the later days of the old Mandatory Palestine, about the extraordinary retrospective matrimonial legislation which had to be introduced to clear the consciences, and legitimize the children, of devout and worthy English people. For years, good men and women had been 'married' by the Anglican Bishop in Jerusalem, before it was discovered by the legalists that they had woefully been living all those years in sin together and producing bastard children. Their fault lay in their not having previously registered a civil marriage with a District Commissioner. This, presumably, was one of those rare cases where retrospective legislation is legitimate, and a happy balm to consciences which long had slept.

Like official statistics, but more often, the incongruous in local advertisements can so often provide amusement for the new-come visitor. As in some places else throughout the world, in hot lands in particular, there is a local decency about the wearing of ties or jackets in restaurants. So it was natural, and only surprising to the uninitiated, to find the advertisement of a floor show called 'Nudema': there, where ladies were to abandon much, was the large-lettered admonition 'Gentlemen will retain their jackets'.

We all must surely recognize the curiosities of costume which spring to the attention as one moves from land to land. The custom of the one is the oddity of the other: here it is you who are odd, and there it is me. If you don't think and feel yourself uncomfortable in costume, then assuredly it is the other fellow who is the oddity, even though he and his sisters outnumber you a thousand to one. If you are a missionary teacher and your cotton vest is primarily a many-coloured Coca-Cola advertisement, it is most certainly your visitors who are odd, coming from the water, by power-boat travel from the city, the women in tight short shorts. And if you are the 'Teach' in another bush village and your vest is emblazoned with 'Everyone loves Peter', then it is no more than a desirable sentiment and probably very true.

However, the visitor to Georgetown is undubitably surprised, the first time that it rains after his arrival, to find what a large proportion of the population wear their mackintoshes backwards. Yet in fact, what a very sensible arrangement! If you are moving forwards—and after all that is usual—then the front of you gets wettest. And if you are riding a bicycle, movement forward is all the faster, and therefore all the more sensible it is to button your mackintosh, gay plastic or otherwise, down your back, and present an unbroken frontal surface to the downpour. It needs to be recognized, too, that bicycles form a most important part of Guiana life, especially in Georgetown, the B.G. capital.

Thirty years ago in Cambridge there was a traditional bicycle, hireable for special occasions, a tandem bicycle for four seated in line astern. All pedalled but one alone controlled the steering. No such phenomenon graces Georgetown's pedal-filled streets. Mechanical advancement still has far to go. Meanwhile the younger—and not so young—of this fair white-painted wooden city, make do with bicycles designed for one, where the central figure is responsible for the steering and all the pedalling too. But that does not mean those two wheels shall only carry one man or woman, girl or boy. The Georgetown practice is a generous one: the primary bicyclist carries others, one, two, three, or even four, not even scorning the pregnant or those permanently large by nature. The skill is remarkable and the wobbling no more than the motorist's normal view of bicycles as stationary objects with an infinite capacity for sideways motion—like rooks teetering on telegraph wires.

Passenger number one is usually seated on a standard carrier behind. Side saddle is usual, more decorous, and more suitable for skirts whether over-tight or bouffant. Side saddle on the bar is common too and perhaps more cosy, while those who wish for converse take the friend seated backwards on the handle-bars. Positions are additive and may be duplicated as demand arises and body size allows. This special social custom gives a gaiety and grace to Georgetown which is surprising, no matter the fears of the timorous motorist unused to massed pedal traffic. The streets of Cambridge provide an adequate background experience, plus perhaps a little luck.

Yet there is one all too obvious group of unfortunates for whom bicycles are sadly beyond their physical competence. A particular feature of the Guianas is the high proportion of the people suffering from filariasis, or, more descriptively, elephantiasis. The visible symptom, the enormous swelling of one, or sometimes both, legs is distressing to see and must be quite frightful to possess. The causative nematode worm is carried by certain biting insects. Prophylaxis now is far advanced and much further research and effort proceed. Yet the visible symptoms take years to mature and then are permanent. The appearance of elephantiasis in the population will thus remain long after that happy day when further infections have become rare. The grossly swollen legs are far more obvious in women because of the nature of their clothes, but whether the disease is really more frequent than in men remains a possibility, a result perhaps of differences in habit between the sexes, in type of work or manner or place of sleeping and exposure to the insect carriers. Oddly enough, and fortunately too, the visitor, even if infected will not develop the final symptom unless he spends many long later years in tropic lands.

The incidence of filariasis is even greater in Surinam than in B.G., in Paramaribo than in Georgetown. One sometimes thinks, for example near the market in Paramaribo, that at least one in twenty of the adult women have evident elephantiasis. It is this high incidence, which leads so often to the wearing of high surgical boots, among these women, in the pathetic attempt to control the approaching gross deformity. Some, in Surinam, suffer operations only less awful than the grossness itself. Long sectors of the elephantic tissue are cut away, rather as if you peeled an orange, then removed alternate segments and sewed the resultant object more nearly to resemble a cylinder than a sphere.

Forty years ago, at the Empire Exhibition at Wembley, there were examples of the ravages of the tropical diseases. There in full display, by photograph and with pickled limbs in jars, were the two great deformers, elephantiasis by the gross addition of tissue to produce legs like those of a rhinoceros, and leprosy where a mere stump results from progressive erosion. The Guianas still have both these horrors, in residual form for medical advance has now gone far. Leprosy is worse, its infectivity requiring isolation, whereas the sufferer from filariasis can remain at liberty. Both may be expected to disappear within a few decades of orderly medical progression, unless other causes, intrinsic in many lands today, create a social chaos in which expertise will die.

Another trouble, in the interior of the Guianas, is the bats and the rabies which they carry. Sleeping nets in many areas are as essential anti-bat as elsewhere anti-mosquito, though it is true that some run the risks of neglect. These bats are suckers of animal blood, vampires, of several species, with sharp incisors which can cut through the skin without waking the sleeper. Pointed parts, nose, elbow or toe, are the usually chosen sites of attack, and a covering of netting, if taut across a leg or arm will not necessarily deter the bat from taking its fill from the sleeping person in the hammock. Even the official antidotes for bat-borne rabies are very beastly, requiring a series of heavy injections in the belly with most unpleasing side-effects. These are to be borne by those who have been attacked or by those, like veterinarians, who suffer special risks. The need for such a powerful and painful antidote is greatly to be avoided by sufficient care.

Yet in the absence of the official antidote, which means amateur action in the bush when medical care is more than forty-eight hours away, the recommended treatment is severe indeed. We travelled with facilities for such personal, or uxorial, treatment, having been duly provided in advance by the kindly Health Service in the University of Cambridge. We carried a sealed tin which contained a sealed bottle of a most powerful liquid. The instructions were, on finding a bat-bite on one's spouse—and standard medical treatment being at a distance—the site should be slit with a knife and the magic fluid poured into the wound. The pain, it was prophesied, would be great and the need was probable that one must sit heavily on one's spouse until the treatment was completed. The treatment with luck would be effective. The pain would indubitably be very great. The magic fluid in the bottle was concentrated nitric acid.

Fortunately matrimonial felicity was never tested with such ferocity and the sealed bottle was handed back intact. It may be hoped that its further journeys will be prolonged and its seals remain unbroken. Such untampered travels remind one of that small cask of salt pork, an ultimate reserve, which we carried all the way on deck and under sail to Antarctica

hirty years ago. It came home, happily, still unbroached, and
vas returned to the ship's chandlers. Its total longevity was
unknown to us but it bore on the bung the informative statement 'resealed 1905'.

The rabid danger is real to man, even if normally avoidable
nd if rather recently appreciated. It is a danger now even
northwards into the United States where bats have lately been
lemonstrated to be potential carriers of the disease. The
primary cycle of this rabies is between cattle and the bats. In
he savannas of B.G., in the Rupununi region adjacent to
Brazil, the disease is a severe check upon economic cattle
aising. The conditions are difficult enough without the
ddition of the disease. In the past the cattle were driven on
he hoof near 300 miles down the cattle trail to the coast. Now
hey are slaughtered at Lethem and the carcasses are immediately flown[1] by Dakota to Georgetown. These savannas
support at present—and whatever may be the potential
increase by upgrading of beasts and pasture, alike—about
0,000 cattle. The annual kill for the market, approaches
,000 beasts, but the annual kill by rabies, it is said, is a figure
ttle different. The opportunity for veterinary control is great
ut undeniably tedious and expensive.

However, filariasis, leprosy and rabies are not killing
iseases in the sense of that ubiquitous malaria which until so
ecently held in check the people of the Guianas; and indeed
till holds in demographic thrall so many in distant lands
hroughout the world. The resultant population surge which
dds such danger to malaria's conquest may be considered
ter. The personal and local effect of malaria eradication is

1 In fact in 1961 and 1962 for many months a border outbreak of
oot and mouth disease resulted in no slaughter and no movement
f cattle from the savannas to the coast, a matter of considerable
ardship to the ranching community.

quite astonishing. So far as B.G. is concerned there has been a spectacular fall in mortality in the post-war years, a fall at all ages but primarily in infancy. Malaria has been almost completely eradicated from the populous coastal region following an intensive campaign actuated and led by Dr Giglioli, the eminent malariologist. The insect vector responsible for the distribution of malaria in this region of watery channels, so much of it empoldered and below high tide mark, was *Anopheles darlingi*. This species was so anthropophil that when, after the war, D.D.T. first became widely available, it was killed by the relatively simple expedient of spraying the internal walls of all inhabited places well nigh simultaneously. The species thus was virtually exterminated and with it the human malarial parasite which it carried. The incredibly numerous school population today owes its existence to Dr Giglioli's competence and zeal.

Fortunately *Anopheles darlingi* was so anthropophil that it could easily be met by chemical means. The other numerous species of local mosquitoes are not lovers of mankind in the same way though they may be capable of transmitting the malarial parasites. Nor are these other species so easily controllable in so watery a land. But there is an inkling now of the emergence of a new problem which may be difficult indeed to solve. Another species of mosquito, *Anopheles aquasalis*, is being set a new problem in its specific struggle for existence, to achieve its requirement, in each generation, of having a drink of good mammalian blood. It is a mosquito which normally and conveniently sucks cattle, horses and other domestic stock, and when these are available has no use for men. But now the numbers of domestic animals fall rapidly and they are less conveniently placed. Town planners get cattle removed from the immediate vicinity of dwelling houses, and some increase of affluence has led to a greater reliance o imported meat and milk. The sugar estates, too, are changing over from animal to mechanical mules for dragging the cane-laden punts along the transport canals. *A. aquasalis* in consequence grows hungry and begins now to experiment with stealing human blood instead. Thus is developing a new biological race of semi-anthropophil mosquitoes diverging from an anthropophobe ancestry. New outbreaks of malaria occur and the solution of this new problem is by no means evident even to the greatest of malariologists. Maybe, like it is said in parts of Indonesia, tethered pigs will have to be kept among the houses as a form of bait.

Like the development of myxomatosis-resistant rabbits, and 'hospital' strains of resistant pathogens, so evolves a new race of malaria-carrying mosquitoes: another new type is in the making, this time an awkward one. Here may be a case where the mosquitoes themselves cannot be controlled and all reliance must be placed upon the limitation of their ravages after the malarial parasites have entered the bodies of men and women. That is done at present by arranging the regular consumption of nivaquine or other suitable drugs. To ensure that this is daily continued throughout normal life, however economically humble the people concerned, the method is for the drug to be mixed with all salt sold, a cheap commodity which all will take, and for which government subsidy may be available. Already this is done in Guiana for balata bleeders and others who work in harsh conditions in the interior.

Looked at more widely one of the most remarkable features of tropical South America is the extent of speciation, the production of innumerable new species of animals and plants within, we are told, geologically quite recent times. The period of modern speciation, some now assert, has occurred mainly within the last few tens or hundreds of thousands of

years in a period of rapid climatic change. That speciation
would seem to continue fast today. The birds, the fish, the
insects and the trees show it in particular. Hosts of closely
similar species exist side by side, each presumably occupying
and exploiting slightly separable ecological niches. This is
not a denial of fast speciation elsewhere in the world but
simply a statement of its particular speed and obviousness in
South America. The abundance of mimetic insects which
enthuse the entomologists, the abundance of the freshwater
fishes which offer themselves to the tropical aquarists, the (in
truth excessive) variety of trees which trouble the timber
trade, all these are reflections of this recent and present phase
of rapid evolution. There is tremendous fascination for the
visiting biologist. Elsewhere probably the greatest assemb-
lages of diverse species co-existing are to be found in active
tropical coral reefs and in the plankton of the world's warm
seas. But in the tropical South American swamps and forests
there is the same phenomenon with creatures and vegetation
large and small at the same time. The impression of the
variety and profligacy of life is tremendous, and most astonish
ing perhaps among the insects.[1] The bewilderment and
astonishment, at the multiplicity of form and species, have
been cried aloud for more than a century by the biological
travellers of South America. The entomologist is in heaven
and even the mammalogist may look through the gates into
another's paradise, his own being all too often so incon-
veniently nocturnal or locked within the forests. The diversity
of insects, some more large and more brilliant in colour or in
mimicry than previously conceived, must be viewed in
collection if perspective is to be attained. Illumination and

1 The finest entomological collections in the region are in the
museum in Paramaribo under the direction of Dr Geijskes, to whose
kindness we are much indebted.

nderstanding are not clarified, only vitalized, by the chance
ntomological encounters of the day's travels. The full per-
ective needs the museum collection.

There, gathered together in stiff array, and pinned and
ehydrated though they be, are huge butterflies and moths,
uge beetles with enormous jaws and probosces, and beetles
ith brilliant tough elytra which Amerindians may still collect
 bunches as decorative rattles for their headdresses. There
isplayed is the actual range of enormous Orthopterans,
cluding in their number remarkable instances of mimicry in
esemblance to leaves, both the living and the dead and, again,
oth the entire and the crumpled or broken. There in the
ollection, side by side in dead and lasting demonstration, are
vo species of slender beetle, the one with a curious tuft of
airs in the middle of its half-inch long antennae while all its
gs are bare. The other species has an identical tuft of hairs on
e back legs while all the other legs and the antennae are
are. There may be, there is the possibility of, a yet ununder-
ood functional basis for this divergence within similarity, or
e we to imagine some chance chromasomal tangling and
bscure embryonic development to produce so surprising an
fect non-functionally?

The collection extends on and on, from drawer to drawer,
ven the biologically educated visitor standing in genuine
mazement at what exists. There is a species of leaf-cutting
t which keeps a midden, for those leaves which are surplus
 requirements, for the cultivation of those fungi upon which
e ants prefer to feed. And in the middens lives a special big
eetle whose larvae grow there and are preyed upon by a
articular kind of snake.

Indeed the radiation and speciation proceeding still today in
is hot region of luxuriance is astonishing. More remarkable
it still if a recent tentative finding is fully confirmed.

Detailed pollen analyses have now been started for this equatorial region of eastern South America, so giving an inkling of the time scale. This work suggests that even so late as only 60,000 years ago this region was occupied by genera and species which we now regard as belonging to temperate lands. If that was really so then, in those millenia, the truly equatorial flora must almost have been pinched, climatically, into non-existence, so making the speciation whose results we now see a matter of very recent evolution indeed.

Come now out of the museum with its fascinating collections of the dead, and watch again the living.

For those who have never seen their like before, the butterflies of Guiana are fascinating beyond measure. Bright oranges and yellows abound in many lands; it is the blueness of the Morpho and its relatives which astonishes in South America. These magnificent creatures, five and six inches across, have often been described, but their marvel, to the newcomer to the shadowy creeks and forests, surely can never pall for fault of previous description. The precise area and hue of blue varies with the species, and it is the male alone which entices the observers' eye, for the females, like hen pheasants, are a dull and rusty brown. In the mystifying alternation of brilliant light beams and dark leaf shadows, the blue splashes of Morpho wings glint and disappear in an astonishing manner. The flight is fast and irregular, and only in particular positions is the blue to be seen from a distance, usually from the side and below, for the creatures tend to fly high.

These vivid blue butterflies appear and disappear like, one could imagine, huge iridescent fireflies, invisible between the glints. They vanish and reappear, now up, then down irregularly from side to side, and rarely can they be flying straight. They are creatures of the forest spaces, ami the shadow and the brightness, and their actual speed in flight, presumably a function of the temperature,[1] is high.

These splendid Morphos cannot be caught by the ardent entomologist, with waving net, however fleet of foot. They must be caught by skill and trickery, by an art which I have never tried myself. There are two methods, the one based on scent and the other upon vision. A fermenting mixture of banana and rum may, with a long stick, be rubbed on a suitable branch at what seems the popular level for flight in the species to be captured. The Morphos apparently quite easily fall to alcoholic temptation; and the drunk of all species are not difficult to outwit. A long-enough-handled net will take the sozzled butterflies as they sit around their sin. Alternatively, one male having been captured—or a small piece of bright plastic may suffice—a fan is decorated with the brilliant blue, then waved in a seductive manner in the forest. Thus may interested females be enticed and competitive males attracted too. Continue waving your blue visual bait with one hand and wave your net skilfully with the other and the Morphos will be yours. Or so I am told.

Return now again a moment from the butterflies, this time to the wasps and an extraordinary example of their use by primitive Amerindians in the depths of Surinam. These people have now, with one small exception, recently risen from their surviving Stone Age culture, and have advanced from hostility

1 In contrast the low ambient temperatures may limit the activity of Arctic insects to an extent such that there may be only three or four days, or even hours, in the whole course of a year when there is warmth enough for active movement and mating. For example, see G. C. L. Bertram on 'The Low Temperature Limit of Activity of Arctic Insects' in the *Journal of Animal Ecology*, Vol. 4, No 1, May 1935.

to friendliness. They retain yet many of their primitive customs, including much use of the tail feathers of macaws for personal decoration and the making of large earthenware pots by coil upon coil of clay. One curious custom still survives, or perhaps stimulating custom is a better adjectival description. Specially woven mats are prepared by the women and then, with the aid of a tube, intoxicated wasps are inserted so that they are caught by their waists in the basket-work. They are arranged alive with the stings all pointing in one direction. Areas of wasp sting mat are then applied upon the bodies of boys, small wasp mats for small boys, and more and more as growth proceeds. Then many are applied simultaneously so that the lad, by not flinching at the pain, may emerge, strengthened, into manhood. The larger mats are about a foot square and may contain nearly 400 living wasps. Elderly Amerindians sometimes therapeutically apply such mats to their own arms, to stimulate and strengthen them, so to revive their accuracy with the bow.

The remarkable speciation of tropical South America is by no means confined to butterflies and other insects, but extends to many groups in varying degrees, even the rodents remarkably among the mammals. The fishes, too, the freshwater fishes of the great rivers and their innumerable tributaries, show an exceptionally high degree of speciation. Compared with the Cyprinid speciation of the African tropical lakes, it is the small Characid fishes which, in South American minor waters, have so proliferated. This indeed is the source of most of those myriad small fishes of so many species which in these days delight the warm-water aquarists of North America and Europe. Caught with fine nets in the Guianas and in Amazonia the little fishes are sorted and packed in bulk by the dealers of Georgetown and elsewhere, for onward flight in oxygen filled plastic bags to the colder cities of the north. The trade is now extensive[1] and the losses in transit are said to be small.

In Europe and in Israel carp have long been sent to market alive in temporary tanks—road vehicles with a water-filled tarpaulin, into which is bubbled oxygen from a cylinder. The advent of plastic bags in the last two decades has allowed an extension of the technique to a world trade in fishes, for commerce and for zoos. The bags, half-filled with water and with oxygen blown in to fill the upper spaces, are sealed and transported in bulk by air. The enclosed captives, like intrepid space men sealed in capsules, are the playthings of forces beyond their immediate control. Panic will pay no dividend and the eager may peer through the transparent walls at the helpless sossing captives. With good fortune and no excessive delays, eventually release will come into a little heated tank far far from the land of origin. In the new home death by predators is unlikely, breeding is often possible, and the pleasure given to the amateur collector or, therapeutically to the patients in the dentist's waiting-room, may be substantial. This seems a world apart from the age-old and possibly still surviving slow transport by junk of fish-fry from China to the growing ponds of Malaya—fish-fry in big wooden tanks whose waters were constantly agitated and oxygenated by men gently patting the surface with little paddles.

But let it not be thought that the fishes of the Guianan and Amazonian rivers are much limited in size. Limited of course they must be, but the limit in fact is higher than anywhere else in the world, the Arapaiama (*A. gigas*) being the greatest of them all. It is apparently no danger at all to man.

1 The value of this export trade, mainly with U.S.A., was said to be about £40,000 in both 1957 and 1958. See 'Review of the Fisheries of British Guiana' in Bulletin No. 1 of the Fisheries Division of the Agriculture Department 1958.

This huge creature, perhaps over nine feet in length,[1] is the largest of all truly freshwater fishes. Indeed there are few marine fish, apart from sharks, and the anadromous sturgeon, which are longer. The Arapaima is an inhabitant of the upper waters of the Amazon system. But it seems that in quite recent times it has got across into the rivers of B.G. This feat is not so remarkable after all, so peculiar are the river systems, and so humble the water shed. Some 1,600 miles from the mouth, the upper fingers of the Amazon system, the Takatu and the Ireng, form the border with B.G. There, in the flat savannas, in fact only a few hundred feet above sea level, not far off are the first tributaries of the Rupununi which flows into the Essequibo and so into the sea between the mouths of the Amazon and the Orinoco. Between the Takatu and the Rupununi the Arapaima have passed in the season of floods, doubtless as young fishes, but capable of immense growth and reproduction to fill the new rivers now open to them. The transfer of habitat has indeed been so successful, from the Arapaima's viewpoint, that now Brazilian hunters troop into B.G. territory to fish. Having greatly diminished, to un-economic levels, the stocks of Arapaima in their own vast territory, now they come unmolested over the borders to denude likewise the Rupunini in B.G. The case for controlling legislation, enforcement, and common-sense management is great. So far the valiant efforts of the few fisheries advisers have not been converted into law despite repeated efforts since 1958.[2]

A particular further interest of this tale, in the present context, is that the manatee of the Amazon basin has, so far, lagged understandably behind the Arapaima in extending its range. So far as is known the Amazonian species of manatee

1 See McCormick L. J. in *Game Fish of the World*. London. 1949.
2 See Appendix I.

has not yet got across from the Takatu river—where it is in fact said to occur—to the Rupununi. Nor is the Rupununi itself said to contain the ordinary manatees of Guiana. Indeed it is not known how far up the Essequibo the manatees occur. The Takatu and the Rupununi both seem in fact rather unpromising for vegetarian mermaids and, lower down, the Essequibo has all too many rapids for their convenience. So it seems likely that what has proved possible for Arapaima will continue to be a barrier for manatees.

Since youth in most of us there has been awareness of stories of men and horses forced to wade or swim across South American rivers. They arrive as skeletons at the far bank, their flesh completely stripped from their bones by the gnashing steely jaws of the dreaded Pirai and the other voracious fishes of those great distant rivers. So it was unexpected, and not with total tranquillity, that one found oneself bathing for pleasure in, for example, an upper creek off the Demerara river, or in a creek of the Takatu on the Brazilian border, a tributary of the mighty Amazon itself. It seems that the dreaded Pirai *(Serrasalmus spp.)*, whose interlocking teeth will sever piano wire traces and consume the hooves of horses —if stories are to be believed—varies much in its activity from time to time and place to place. In the upper Amazonian tributaries it may well be present, but where less hungry or where no person in memory has been eaten, then that place is locally thought fit for swimming. It is the stranger who suspects, and expects his toes to be severed by Pirais; who fancies a water kamoudi, a huge constrictor snake, will enwrap his neck; who imagines that the cercarial larvae of deadly flukes will enter through his tight-pursed lips; or that sting-rays and electric eels will poison and shock him to extinction. The first swim is followed by others with a waning fearfulness. The sandy bottom reflects the over-river pattern of bright sunlight and dark leaf shadows; the clear dark water refreshes heated limbs and body; the buttress roots wall the creek, and dangling water-searching roots hang down from high above; orchids and Bromeliads, huge pods and lanceolate leaves, all add a fantastic roofing to the happy bathing creek. Yet, and yet again, to the newcomer, the zoologist versed in possibilities, there lurks a suspicion that some, or just one, of the possibilities will turn into a present fact. This lurking suspicion keeps at somewhat more than arm's length that tranquillity of mind which should accompany swimming at its best.

Remember that a fascinating aquatic stage in our rather recent evolution has been, perhaps jocularly, postulated by Professor A. C. Hardy of Oxford. Some might find further evidence for his hypothesis in the very special delights which we may gain from particular watery occasions. Such may linger long in memory, being available for happy recollection in the years which follow. There are two chief features, the tactile tranquillizing of the body, and the subtle pleasuring of the eye which, combining and reacting, can achieve that perfection which totally satisfies. There are further fascinations like the tickling of toes by little fishes in the shallows, the calls of birds, and the flower scents from the land. But the watery touch and the pleasing of the eyes are chief.

It happens, necessarily, that the full satisfaction of the eye needs time and stillness, and therefore the water must be warm. The dip in the glacier lake—ice cliffs and sunshine, vigour and swiftness—may meet the need of a moment. But there is no time for prolonged admiration of the visual scene, no time for reflection: it is too cold for stillness and contemplation. So it is from among the warmer swims of one's travels that one selects the special samples to be recollected, re-lived and contrasted.

Oddly enough Iceland affords one memory most vivid, good

in visual worth, but very special indeed in bodily sensation. A pool lies open to the sky, the distant mountains and the screams of terns: there one learns the meaning of the optimum. At one end flows in a frigid stream, at the other the subterranean product of a hot spring, slightly sulphurous and very warm. Somewhere amid the mixing of the two is the place to float in optimal tranquillity. A stimulating and sometimes startling search precedes success, but then comes free flotation as in Paradise; sensation of temperature vanishes; and the body lies in peace as a vehicle for the eyes for scenic admiration.

Again make use of a hot spring, in the Sea of Galilee, on its western side, close to the rocks now covered with alien Bougainvilia over which by tradition dashed the Gadarene swine those many centuries ago. Swim there in winter, the warm waters rising through the pool's clear gravel floor and seeping out into the lake whose coolness affords the foil to present pleasure. Float there and rest content, your eyes fastened upon snow-capped Mount Hermon, those miles away across the lake. Float there at rest, the warm sunshine upon the baldness of your head. And, if the day is ornithologically propitious, a flight of pelicans, with steady beats of their enormous wings, will cross the line of sight between Hermon and your toes.

Inland again, to savour a recollection from a temperate river. It is Provence in August and the River Gard. The water's temperature is perfection, and the noblest arches of the Roman era span the summer sky. The swiftness of the stream discourages free floating, so wallow in the shallows and seek an anchorage of rock. Then lie in admiration of the work of men's hands two millennia ago. Three tiers of arches recede in size as they mount above you to the clouds. Tall poplars parallel the bridge's feet, the greenness of the trees in pleasing contrast to the honey colour of the stones. The reflecting blueness of the river flows down the gorge so far below the topmost thwartwise channel which once carried the crystal water of the Fontaine de l'Eure to the people of Nîmes. The architectural marvel of the past powerfully impresses its visual magnificence upon the joyful swimmer of today.

Then, from light into darkness or near it—from sun-baked Provence to the Suez Canal where a swim by night may have its special peculiarity. The water is warm enough to satisfy and to be forgotten. It is the astonishing phosphorescence which affords the lasting memory, a phosphorescence exceeding that seen anywhere else—in arctic, antarctic or tropic seas. Naked bodies glitter with fire beneath the water; raised arms have globules of fire dripping free from the elbows; every watery turbulence turns to swirling specks of phosphorescent flame. And then come porpoises close alongside, grunting and playing, their long black bodies perfectly outlined in moving fire, and leaving a wake of flame gently twisting behind them.

So may one move about the world, sampling the waters by measurement of bodily pleasures, the quality infinitely varied. Too often highest potential quality is spoiled by some small special feature—the little lurking fear of sharks or riverine predaceous fish, the eye-sting from too high salinity, the feet sinking into under-lying chill. But when perfection comes so much the greater joy. Quality is the basis of all appreciation, and the study of comparative quality in recollection is the ploy of times which follow.

In the water is the place for contemplation: and often it is in swimming that one notices most one's hands. It is thus I see my own, those strong wrinkled servants of my fifty years. They are marked by the generality of my way of life, the skills learned by effort and the special incidents and accidents of time. Thus, one may suppose, he who could discern sufficiently could read the development of a man's whole character and history. To view one's hands and ponder is to bring back memories of many days from early youth and onwards, and the memories of incidents, usually mildly injurious, and the settings in which the damage was received. In earlier days those hands were softer, pinker, hairless and with no finger bound by golden marriage ring. The tip of the left index finger went at age eleven when playing in a bedroom with a razor blade set in a meccano handle. The damage was not severe and the shape returned with time. But much blood was spilled and there was a walk to the doctor with a hand raised on high like those Hindu holy men who by willpower immobilise and allow to shrink an arm which is held permanently aloft to the greater glory of God. The small scars inevitably increase with the passage of the years. There is the mark of the careless blade, deep between thumb and forefinger, when the bluish-silvery ligaments were momentarily visible before the blood came welling out. That was when whittling a stick for fishing. There is the mark of the slivered skin from the forefinger—the left hand is usually the sufferer—when the blunt knife was sharpening a wooden spike in that small antarctic schooner in St Katharine's Dock. There are the marks of sawcuts on the knuckles. There are marks on the tips, torn on coral reefs. There is the starry scar from a curious purulent infection whose central pea-like greenish mass eventually came loose when swimming in sight of Mount Carmel and the mosque of Acre. But mine have been lucky hands; there are no digits nor phalanges gone, and nails lost have all returned. Those splits along the outsides of the fingers, caused by excessive hauling on hard ropes at sea, have long since disappeared.

All these marks are the nostalgic trifling things of days gone by. The appearance, strength and thickness of the hands and fingers, they are the integration of heredity and the way of life. With mine there is sadly no sign of superb manual dexterity of any sort. Rather is there an earthiness—a term less harsh than grubbiness—an earthiness truly connected with the soil. But these, my servants, can yet continue to learn. At forty they learnt to milk and at forty-seven to cold-shoe horses. Yet, to confess, some of their strength has gone by default: that test, the curling of crown stoppers between thumb and forefinger of one hand unaided, now is a labour for the right while the left hand can succeed no longer.

All this digression sprang from aquatic pleasure and watery contemplation—and so now to return to them.

The sensations afforded by water surfaces are immensely varied, from the swelling vastness of the storm-swept Southern Ocean to the spangled calmness of the tropic creek. Not only are there pleasures and pains of the body associated with water particularly in high latitudes, but there are deep aesthetic sighs of contentment, or cries of nostalgia in one's breast, in the mere contemplation of still waters. Maybe there yet resides in us a vestigial love or longing for that aqueous environment which for so many millions of years was the home of our remote ancestors. Yet in this powerful aesthetic visual pleasure in the waters, it is not only the substance that delights the eye, but the associated organisms. The shapes and colours of the plants, the company and elegance of birds, the flit and dart of gaily patterned insects, all these fill one with a combined seething of the spirit and contentment of the mind.

The Guianas afford much scope for thought, much water for pleasuring, much vegetation to entrance one in its watery environment. Water lilies may be cultivated in a wide spread of latitudes, but for best effect they should be grown in tanks at waist level so that one may peer closely into their anther-filled floating cups. But the Guianas naturally possess, from their Amazonian proximity, one of those enormous species of water lily whose leaves spread several feet across (*Victoria amazonica*). The new leaves rise from the bottom like pink prickly cricket balls on vertical stalks. Then they gradually unfurl at the surface, the pinkness and the prickliness forming the underside of the enlarging, floating, high-rimmed saucer whose centre is a smooth pale green. No need here for the elongate toes of lily-trotting birds—maybe a man with skis could freely walk across the contiguous adult leaves.

Then lotus leaves and flowers—a species whose origin is in the Orient—can afford extraordinary pleasure after rain. The very slightly glaucous leaves become as green crucibles holding beads of molten silver, and the wind turns the beads to rivulets which spill from the swaying foliage. The flowers are pink and cream and the ovary at first a waxy yellow. This swells as the petals fall to become a handsome green and conical mace before drying to a brown container filled with purplish seeds set in their separate compartments. The wind on lotus beds turns silvery the leaves by presentation of their undersides. The joys of lotus-eaters, in visual contemplation, must have been superb, but their diet—the seeds it must be supposed—does not attract. One wonders, too, how lotus eaters, lolling in moist places, defended themselves against ants and biting flies. Poetic imagery is often more pleasing than reality. A particular reality of another sort is the record held by the seeds of lotus (*Nelumbo nucifera*) for anabiosis— longevity in a dormant state. Lotus seeds have germinated successfully after a wait of over a thousand years in a peat bog.[1]

As well as waters, the search for manatees, unexpectedly but very pleasantly, leads into places of great trees. It is not that the manatee creeks are invariably lined by trees, nor that the manatees themselves penetrate the forests. When there is shade, there is an absence of soft succulent food weeds, and

1 See *Nature* No. 4842, p. 643. 18 August 1962.

the manatees do not dwell there. But the lands where manatees live, the Guianas, have trees of great variety and they are inevitably available and pleasure-giving to any traveller who will accept that pleasure. The prodigality of the tropical forest in species is great and is well known. The appreciation of tree form in forests however is often difficult for, except in very special forests of pillar-like timber and little undergrowth, the individual trees cannot properly be observed. The new opportunity comes where heavy bush has been removed over the years, as it has been over large areas of cultivation, for then single special trees remain. Often in the Guianas these are huge silk-cotton trees which the people have had a certain reluctance to fell, and for which they appear to have feelings akin to reverence. Once spared in the initial clearance the giant may prosper on for many years, shade-giving and unspoilt, adding character to the country and pleasure to the traveller.

These huge single trees can be seen for miles across the coastal plains; they form focal points when travelling along the meandering rivers; often they carry from their crowns the swinging pursed and woven nests of brightly coloured mocking birds. But it is the very shapes of the trees which give most pleasure; the grey upstanding trunk, so stalwart in its strength and so admirably supported and anchored by its flanging buttress roots; the crown composed of a few huge branches, horizontal and then upward curving, seeming to embrace the sky. One giant, alone among the scrub, amid the fruit bearing trees or within a palm-thatched village, may cast a deep shadow from its leafy head, while another may be bare at the same season so that its load of epiphytes seems temporarily out of place, baking in the sunshine.

One such huge tree stands upon the bank of the Suriname river at Brokopondo. That tree can be seen to most special advantage because from a veranda in a rocky place above, one can look down upon it at just that angle which still allows appreciation of height and form yet also allows one's eyes to rest upon the foliage. Behind the tree is the river and immediately beyond the river is the steep forest rising to the hilltops, a forest flecked with vertical silvery streaks, the stems of tall false-pawpaws and other species. The special tree, the beautiful giant silk-cotton tree, is the home of a colony of black and scarlet birds. Their fathom-long pursed nests swing in all the winds, and the gregarious chattering birds fly from branch to branch arguing, flirting, building and flying everywhere for more fine nesting materials fit for weaving. Too often we crane our necks and see birds dully against the sky, their colours consequently in shadow. But watching these red and black mocking birds from above one sights their scarlet rumps brilliantly in full sunshine. Just so can one sometimes see the full glistening beauty of pigeons from a cathedral tower, or five swans flying low in sunshine over the green Backs of Cambridge against a curtain of autumnal gold. Likewise the English chestnut tree in flower, splendidly laden with blossom when seen from the side, has a quite astonishing profusion of white candles when seen from above. That is how to view a flowering tree: get above it on a day of sunshine. That is how best to appreciate the mocking birds and hangnests. Yet, remember, that now tranquil river beneath the hang-nests' tree has recently been the place of death of two men, utterly devoured by predaceous Pirai, within minutes and without chance of rescue.

In contrast with the beauty of the individual tree there is the colour pattern of the forests seen from aircraft. There is no dull uniform green but countless shades of green, dark and shadowed, emerald and glistening. There are occasional trees which have shed their leaves as if apeing the deciduous species of more temperate lands. There are tall grey stems shooting through the green luxuriant mat of lesser trees to hold their crowns alone above the mass. And the whole is dotted, according to season, with bright jewels, individual trees in flower, yellow, lilac, scarlet, bronze and white. The scarlets in particular are not always flowering trees but often are masses of scarlet flowering creepers which have reached the treetops to luxuriate in the sunshine above. If one could but promote a forest floral expedition by helicopter, so as to descend, and study the individual trees! Treetop platforms would be built for the making of extended observations in peace, for the noise and wind from the rotors would soon drive one mad. Ingenious people in Malaya have practised 'monkey botany' with trained monkeys who run aloft and bring down particular fruits and flowers. Yet the tropical forests contain so very many species that new techniques of survey are still needed so as to assess timber potentiality and species distribution alike.

Apart from many economic and other factors, one special problem of tropical forestry is that the trees, like the animals and other plants of hot lands, run to an immense variety of species rather than, as in colder climates, large numbers of individuals of a much smaller number of species. The latter is far easier for exploitation, and for the organizations of regeneration too. Greenheart is a case in point, that remarkable timber, product of Guiana, which for generations has provided the best and heaviest-duty timber for so many purposes. Greenheart, like some others, is so dense that it sinks in water: its transport by river requires additional flotation by lighter logs lashed alongside or by suspension in bundles from special boats. Greenheart has been so valuable a timber that great areas have been exploited for it alone, or in conjunction with a small number of other highest-grade species. The reserves of commercially exploitable Greenheart in B.G., at present rates of taking, are said now to provide for no more than a further few decades. The problems of Greenheart regeneration have only recently been solved so that present exploitation remains comparable with mining rather than with harvesting.

A personal and lasting interest in Greenheart was stimulated now nearly thirty years ago by its specialized use for the sheathing of wooden polar ships. In 1934 we set off in the last small sailing vessel[1] equipped for antarctic coastal survey and the navigation of its surrounding areas of pack ice. In an English shipyard her elderly, hundred-foot-long Breton, oaken hull was sheathed with three inch planks of Guianan Greenheart which will not splinter under the crash of ice. That timber worthily performed the task.

The fascination of forestry is very great for those in other disciplines, who share the same spirit and long term interest, and possess the realization that future prosperity depends upon the harvesting of plant and animal stocks in a manner that shall be biologically rational. Quite properly the heads of forestry departments are styled 'Chief Conservator of Forests', for conservation is their task. The ignorant still regard conservation of forests as being opposed to the use of forests. The more discerning, those educated to some semblance of common sense, recognize that so much present exploitation of forests is ephemeral—the mining of the existing timber and then a move elsewhere—in comparison with the conservation of forests which means the limitation of annual exploitation to a level which represents the actual growth of woody material year by year. Forest conservation is perpetual rational exploitation so that the same area may produce a useful harvest from one generation to another.

In this connection it needs recognition that world

1 R. S. S. Penola of the British Graham Land Expedition 1934–7.

requirements of wood and wood products are both constantly increasing and constantly changing. Some acute shortages are already felt, and in any event world forest resources are badly distributed in relation to centres of consumption. Many natural forests have low production, and the wood produced is not in much demand. The tropical forests are typified by luxuriance and variety of growth to an extent which makes them economically a poor proposition, for many species are hard, heavy and difficult to season and are indeed unsaleable. Greenheart, in a sense a luxury timber with very special uses, is an exception to this general picture. Even in Europe large areas of lower grade oak forest, which used to meet demands for fuel and constructional timber, have now become economically a burden on the market. A line of advance[1] must be to improve the productive efficiency of forests all over the world by growing more intensively those species in greater demand. Present expectation is that coniferous soft woods will be in much greater demand than the tropical hardwoods. General purpose timbers are required which are at the same time suitable for making plywoods, chipboards and pulp. The tropical forests are weak in this regard, and the forests of Guiana fit into this general world pattern. The problem is a severe one.

In connection with timber extraction certain narrow cuts through the forest are often needed, but for the building of all-weather roads for heavy transport wide swathes must be laid low. That process has a horrid fascination, a blending of sadness at the rude cutting through of a virgin area of climax forest with awe at what a few men can do with the aid of modern machinery. Anything can be done with power and resources enough, even roads through the Greenland ice cap,

1 'Choosing Forest Species'. *Nature*, 7 July 1962, No. 4836, p. 28. Report on paper by Professor M. V. Laurie of the University of Oxford in Span 5, No. 1, 1962.

oads cut as gullies in the ice, crevasses filled by bulldozed
ompacted snow and icy spoil, the whole roofed over to form
lasting tunnel immune from blizzards and other interference.
urinam shows too the might of many machines used with a
rodigal spirit, for example in the building of the huge earth
am at Affobakka and the scores of miles of dedicated road to
ed the project from the north. That is the American contri-
ution to the great Suralco project wherein the Aluminum
ompany of America and Surinam government come together
r the exploitation of bauxite and its refinement with the aid
f locally-produced hydro-electric power.

But more fascinating in a way is another cutting through
e Surinam forest, a cutting by Surinam government with the
id of Dutch engineers, more elderly machinery, much smaller
esources and a spirit of zeal in the development of a simple
nd. Less than 100 men seemed to be driving a road through
e untouched high forest at the rate of nearly a kilometre a
ay. This development was the work of a few brains and a few
killed men, machine operatives, very far removed from the
vomen and earth-filled baskets' type of development in the
rient.

Stereo air photography had allowed the prior plotting of the
oute despite the low relief of this gently undulating and
otally forest-clad area. A cut, two metres wide and made by
en with cutlass, saw and axe, was driven like a pilot drill
head of the widening operation next to follow. Then came the
ulldozers, just two or three, big yellow monsters[1] widening
e initial cut, pressing into the forest, the jungle, the tangle
f creepers hanging from the epiphyte-encrusted trees of so
any species mixed together. In the shallow soil the trees
arely exceed three feet in diameter and the bulldozers press
nd bang and topple, or cut away the buttress roots with the

1 In fact elderly Caterpillar D.7s.

blade tip until the main stem can be forced to fall. The foremost machine would clear a spear-shaped space pursuing the guiding survey cut. And then the following two or three machines would press the prostrate timber, trash, branches, earth, bird's nests, snakes, spiders, and all else sideways to form a tangled mutilated wall of disarray at the sides of the advancing 100-yard wide clearance floored with tumbled grey-brown earth.

So the cleared ribbon advanced into the forest, a grey ribbon of turmoil and tangled residues, but quickly to be followed by an advancing red ribbon of smoothed ferrite-surfaced road. The bulldozers are followed by earth-movers and scrapers which drag and cut the soil forwards from the ridge tops to fill the intervening shallow valleys, so cutting down through the grey topsoil of the forest to the brown and harder substrate beneath. Then that is capped by the surfacing ferrite moved from the tops of certain hillocks and ridges. So advances the finished road by nearly a kilometre a day. A thirty-yard wide, hard and surfaced road, bordered by further thirty-yard wide strips cleared of all vegetation.

The smaller watercourses are crossed by fills of moved earth pierced by simple concrete conduits. The larger gullies are spanned by wooden bridges made on the spot from newly-felled adze-squared timber. As the advancing bulldozers come upon the higher-quality hardwood species the individual tree laid low is separated from the mass to serve this more exalted purpose. Again, in bridge building, the number of men concerned is very small but their personal skill and effort high. One foreman so employed was a person of remarkable physical form. From behind he seemed a huge gorilla as he bent straining over his auger, a being so powerful, so black, so nearly naked and shining with sweat that his humanity seemed distant. Yet face to face he was a smiling man of charm with glistening teeth and aluminium protective hat, a man of superb strength, zeal and vigour, a leader in the building of timber bridges in the midst of the forest of Surinam. Such are the local men who truly develop an emerging land, not the many and unskilled, the gregarious seekers after imported goods who shout political slogans in their ignorance and drink.

Thus flows the new road through the interminable forest, a red streak through the green, aerially visible from afar, a necessity for rational territorial development, a sadness for naturalists, a permanent barrier perhaps for forest-loving monkeys.

Yet even South American forests do have of course a further edge. Beyond, in western B.G. is the high savanna, a land of scattered Amerindians, of xerophilous plants and the widest of prospects. The boundary between forest and savanna is sharp on a small scale map but irregular on a large, like the boundary between Scotland and the Atlantic ocean. In flight the transition seems abrupt. But once the everlasting forest has been found to have a further edge then the new savanna seems to stretch forward and again interminably. And that is what it does; far far forwards onwards into Brazil the open land extends, undulating, with eminences flat-topped, lacking in strong colours, even dull except for its immensity. To those reared in the forests, with leaf walls close at hand rather than terrestrial horizons, the immensity of the savannas must be frightening. Just as frightening was the sea, even to adult educated refugees from central Europe, on beholding first that which covers four-fifths of the globe. Those who have never before seen the distances have inevitably an unease— akin perhaps to that which may on occasion seize most of us when we contemplate the vastness of the universe, ponder the continuous range from the infinitely small to the immensely large, and strive to understand the everlasting flow of time.

The present point of conscious personality seems utterly irrelevant, within the immensity which spreads in all directions—until there is remembrance of the utter improbability of the actual existence of life, that self-perpetuating capacity of rare and complex carbon compounds. To behold, in adult life for the first time, the ocean, or the savanna, or any new wide horizoned aspect of the earth, must be an astonishing experience. Yet it is indeed probable that of all the 3,000 million co-existing members of our species, and despite the fact that probably a half of them all live no more than a few hundred feet above sea level, the proportion who have actually seen the sea remains still quite small. Likewise, certainly much less than half, it must be judged, have ever in their whole lives been so much as one hundred yards distant from all others of their own species. All this however is a digression from the realization of the immensity of the high savannas of B.G. and Brazil, and the pleasing of the eye with distant perspectives.

The visual pleasures of the Guianas are, however, in sharp contrast with the auditory horrors. Apart from drums in Africa's darkest forests, and gongs in jungle villages, man-made noise is all too often a horrid measure of an increase in the so-called standard of living. Georgetown is a prime example of increasing, excessive and stupid urban noise, which certainly militates against an efficiency which is rarely prominent. Pedal bicycles are sensible and silent, and of these Georgetown has a multiplicity only rivalled by Cambridge, Copenhagen and Rotterdam. But now more motor-cycles monthly emerge through the activities of import agents attempting to meet a local demand married to a novel availability of cash or credit. Small internal combustion engines, world-wide, are permitted to make more noise than large ones, and the power-lusts of the juveniles are stimulated by the racket of machinery between their legs. Those with cars tend to drive at speeds unsuited to Guianan roads, to the detriment of their tyres and the magnification of the accident statistics. But far worse is the insensate hooting of car drivers as they wait outside schools for the emergence of many coloured tots in uniform. If the hooting were by code so that a child, like a lamb, could recognize the appropriate adult, there might be forgiveness, but the random hooting of the many gives to the visitor an impression of overwhelming stupidity—and that is sad, because it is untrue.

The man-made stupidity of hooting horns may be contrasted with the astonishing ullulations of the Howler Monkeys, those red-faced denizens of the forests. So exciting to the visitor, perhaps so tedious to the cognoscenti wearily lying in their hammocks after days of hard geologizing, the pulsating roarings of the Howler Monkeys are astonishing, coming as they do from so small a creature. The adult Howler Monkey is in size perhaps comparable with a well-grown year-old child. The purpose of the roarings may be guessed, as belonging to love, courtship, loneliness or anger. But there is no doubt whence comes the roar and what is the mechanism. The adult Howler Monkey possesses an astonishing extension of the hyoid apparatus, a hollow bony chamber, in the throat, the size of a lemon or a goose egg. The sides of the mandibles are greatly enlarged as wings, developed one supposes, to protect and contain it. In proportion, a human similarly fitted would have a 'howl' the size of a quart pot: such a one would be invaluable as a cheer leader in the trans-atlantic football cult. Though both are Primates, procurement of such a prodigy by hybridization is improbable.

This monkey's howl box has an especial and unexpected cosmetic use among certain of the surviving Amerindians of Surinam. This convenient smooth-walled container is used as a store for certain rare and long thin grass seeds. These seeds are provided with a barbed hook which presumably helps natural distribution of the species by clinging to the hair of passing creatures. But the Amerindians use the seeds singly, in place of forceps, to pluck out one by one their facial hairs. So does the Howler Monkey's howl supplement, one supposes, individual and sexual distinction in life with, after death, the private beautification of Amerindian man and woman.

If the Howler has the largest voice, the little Sakiwinki, the Squirrel Monkey, has reputedly the largest brain in proportion to body size of all earth's creatures, not even excepting man. Perhaps with such equipment the Sakiwinki thinks thoughts more deep than most of us, but in observation its behaviour seems to be much along the usual line of the Primates as a whole. Life in a troupe—in a many-specied forest, with flowers and fruits and insects in great variety and profusion, with macaws and ibis above and hosts of lesser birds at lower levels, with shower and sunshine, love and fear—such Sakiwinki life must be filled with stimulus and interest. If your brain is bigger than other peoples' so much the greater chance, one may presume, of appreciation of all around. Perhaps all this is far too anthropomorphic. But even if it is, that does not detract from the quality of the human pleasure—at dawn and sitting silent in a canoe in a forest creek—derived from the bankside passage of a troupe of little grey and yellow monkeys. The attractiveness of a yellow, red or golden crown of hair is known to all of us, but only in monkeys is it combined with the elegance of a long tufted tail. Attractiveness and elegance together make most pleasing gracefulness— that is to say in the physical sense, for to speak of a Sakiwinki full of grace would be to imagine its possession of much more than that fine large brain alone can warrant.

It is perhaps surprising—it has certainly been disappointing

—that one can travel so far in the world, can travel to all seven continents, and see so many lands and makes of men, and yet fail to achieve, until now, the sight of another species of Primate at ease in its natural haunt. That 'at ease' had to be inserted for accuracy of record, because once in Somaliland a group of wild baboons was sighted as they fled from the harsh grinding of the motor transport. Now at last, in the Guianan forest the Sakiwinkis were at ease, playing and chirruping, nibbling, fighting and brachiating—but not swinging by prehensile tails, an activity for which even the hugeness of the English vocabulary seems to have no verb which springs to mind. The prehensile tail is an attribute possessed by some only among the South American monkeys, an attribute lacking in all their Old World relatives. Grace and agility, ease and facility in the forest, owe much to this addition to the four standard limbs.[1] As the old advertisements used to say—'plus a little something some others haven't got'.

The dawn mist is all about the trees, and their epiphytes grow on and their long roots and creepers are dependent from their branches. The onomatopoeic sound of macaws is more excitingly audible than is their blue and yellow plumage visible, except in glimpses far too brief. Dark yet clear still water, floating grass and lilies, no noise at all save the birds and the Sakiwinkis and the distant roar of Howler Monkeys— all these add to the forested enchantment at the beginning of the new day.

Movement by boat, whether silently by paddle or all too noisily by internal combustion engine, along these narrow creeks and channels has a rare quality almost as of floating in a

1 It is said that 'spider monkeys can hold food with one hand, pick more with one foot, put food in the mouth with another hand and keep on walking with the other foot and tail'. (From label in the Georgetown Museum.)

dream. In a distant way there is a curious similarity with travel over snow in conditions now called 'white-out'. The central feature, the strange similarity, is the seeming absence of an horizon so that sense of distance and of level have jointly vanished. In the creeks and rivers, whether through true forest or merely overgrown with bush, the sylvan arch is complete and the contrasts are great between flecks and shafts of brightest sunshine and the deep opacity of the much more extensive areas of shadow. The water ahead is glassy calm and dark and totally reflective of the brilliant spots of sunlight. So is excluded any quick discernment of that line where actuality meets mirrored imagery. One glides smoothly into a speckled tunnel, seeming to move along its central axis without obvious means of support. It is true that the speckled tessellation is chiefly above, and mirrored, below, and that the sides of the tunnel are banded by connected and reflected vertical stems and buttress flanges, yet there is no firm horizon to steady the eye and to help its interpretation of the unfamiliar. So one paddles gently forward ethereally in midstream, or is it in mid-air, seemingly unsupported, seemingly in a dream, while the flashes of light through shade, to others, gives a reminder of the dazzles of a migraine. It is only on turning back, to view the boat's wake and the lap of wavelets on the buttress roots, that the actuality of a visible horizon suddenly makes obvious the fact that one is proceeding along a tunnel filled exactly halfway up with water.

The old accounts of the Guianas refer regularly to travel by corial, that term including dug-out canoes of all sizes, from the slim crescentic shell, just enough for a single fisherman or traveller, up to large craft for use in warfare. The transport of many men and women and children together, likewise, used to be performed by large corials, in whose cargo would be included not only the cassava equipment and other household necessities, but a load of dogs, tame monkeys, parrots and other birds. Today the term corial survives, especially in Surinam, but the dug-out craft, made from a single log, are very rarely larger than will comfortably carry five or six people at the most. Larger boats in these days are all plank built.

The small dug-out canoe is still ubiquitous, often slim and elegant in shape, beautifully pointed and crescentic and very true. The shell is thin and thwartless, and all surfaces, within and without, have been lightly charred for purposes of hardening and, presumably, preservation too. These corials seem to be of far higher quality than, for example, those dug-out canoes which one meets all along the coasts of the Red Sea and Southern Arabia, dug-outs which in fact are imported, to those arid treeless lands, from India beyond. The corials are altogether slimmer and lighter; but then they are not called upon to make the hard sea passages, and fishing trips to distant reefs which are quite commonly, and quite calmly too, undertaken by the wiry seamen of the Arabian coasts.

The corials of Guiana today show, most convincingly, a particular feature in the evolution of boats. It has long been recognized how a simple dug-out canoe, in many parts of the world, can become the foundation—almost a hollowed keel— for something larger. Planks may be applied to heighten the original gunwales, planks applied singly or in tiers. Some of the quite large seine boats, of the Batinah coast of Muscat and Oman, are of this form, the planks being leather- or fibre-sewn for fastening. But the embryo, which grows to such mature size, is in fact a simple dug-out canoe, even though the finished boat is rowed by eight or, as I have seen, ten primitive oars on either side. [1]

1 J. Hornell, *Water Transport: its Origins and early Evolution*. 1946.

The simple corials of Guiana may often be found with a single tier of planking to enlarge them, but what is novel—or at least not seen by me elsewhere—is adaptation to the use of an outboard engine. This is ingenious and eminently sound and effective. The basic corial is curtailed by a few feet and a strong transom fitted in the gap. Then the added planking is allowed to extend to form a new, more distant, pointed stern, but leaving a gap without a bottom. There squats the outboard engine, protected nicely from the sides, and yet with space enough for tilting and lifting as required. The arrangement seems both sound and sensible.

It is interesting, too, to note the manner in which outboard engines are properly, and so very sensibly, appreciated now as being true aids to efficiency by quite simple, indeed primitive, people. Travelling by plank-built police boat with outboard engine deep into the narrow forest creeks off the Suriname river one may come to an Amerindian village with the little foreshore almost littered by tiny corials. Go on again, deeper into the forest, and reach a Bush Negro village. There the men may chance to be away, logging probably, while the half-naked women, dark, energetic and smiling, allow the peering visitors to admire their rough leaf-thatched wall-less huts, or watch them picking over the rice in hollowed and decorated wooden platters. Most seems, indeed is, so very primitive, yet these people know just what will really help them in life. So money is saved and there, behind a hut and on a wooden stand, is the result—a fine large outboard engine, shiny in its newness, and with a red plastic cover. That purchase represents real good sense and a real increase in the standard of living. It is extraordinary, once you have the means, how much muscle power may be replaced by a little cup of petrol.

It may be recognized that many of the more primitive people in the Guianas, Amerindians and Bush Negros, are just at this nascent stage. New money begins to be available and it is channelled into the purchase of articles that are efficient, sensible and raise life's true level, not just increase the sum of material possessions. The area presents real opportunity for the export trade of metropolitan lands, providing imports to the Guianas which are worthy, not just desirable because novel and coming from a distance. Three diverse examples may be mentioned where trade is already considerable but where the sales may yet be much increased. The first is the outboard engine: their costs are high but the sales already are considerable, and will soon be greater still. Their maintenance, or lack of it, is such that replacement is not often over-long delayed. The second example is brassières, whose usefulness is quite evident to primitive people once practicability has been brought to their attention. In the Guianas trade is good.

The third example that may here be mentioned is gumboots. Their value is great to many, much more from the aspect of physical protection than any thoughts of wetness as in lands which are cold and drear. Trade seems to prosper, but one well may feel that the boots themselves need further evolution, in recognition of this true change of function. It is, among others, the cane-cutters who suffer so much from foot and lower-leg injuries as they toil in the fields. The problems of heat and sweat, together with sure-footedness when heaving big bundles of cane, must be met, in an advanced boot, as well as sheer protection against the mis-swung cutlass and the sharp stabs and spears of the cane already cut. There are other hazards too, for instance snakes, despite the customary burning of the trash in the fields before ever the cutting of the cane begins.

The cane workers, and the rice farmers, are in truth a group of the population of B.G. to which great attention must be paid. These people of peninsular Indian origin, these rural workers, have a present standard of living which is much lower than that now common in the towns yet, nevertheless, already higher than in most tropical areas among agricultural workers. The cane-cutters' labour, conjoined with exotic expertize and capital, results in the export of some 300,000 tons of sugar each year, high-cost sugar though it is on the world scale. This is the country's primary agricultural export producing over a half of the value of the country's output and giving direct employment to over 25,000 people. Next in importance comes bauxite, a production operation which requires proportionately very little labour. The cane workers are the largest homogenous section of the whole population, homogenous alike ethnically, sociologically and politically. They are also the fastest breeding section of the community and fecundity is the primary factor in the whole Guianan situation today whether our interests lie with mermaids, manatees or men. The last inevitably dominate the future of the others.

5

~~~~~~~~~~~~~

Conservation:
The Problem in the Guianas

MEN DOMINATE everywhere, with few exceptions indeed. Men dominate the manatees: they do not compete in the sense of both requiring the same space or the same products of the environment. Men in the Guianas are not even predators of the mermaids in the sense that manatees *must* be killed for food. Certainly some are so killed and nourish those who eat them. And there would be nothing intrinsically wrong with that were manatees still present in their former abundance. The modern problem is that of protecting a now much depleted stock of manatees from, on the one hand the dangers of human fecklessness based on a vestigial hunting pleasure, and on the other from the inevitable disturbance caused by man's mechanical evolution. There is a constant interplay of the quantitative factors concerned. When manatees were many and men were few, human predation was bearable by the stock of mermaids. When men increased predation gradually became excessive: the annual increase of the manatee stock by reproduction was insufficient and the total was diminished. The residual stock of manatees now cannot properly bear even a small degree of predatory activity on the part of a small proportion of the now greatly exaggerated, indeed locally explosive, human population.

What might be the fundamental breeding rate of manatees we have quite insufficient knowledge to conclude. Of men and women we know much in contrast. Human females begin to breed at age fifteen, or thereabouts, according to local custom. They can produce one child a year for a couple of decades or even more and the sexes are born in roughly equal numbers. When the natural modes of human mortality have been largely checked or removed by sanitary, medical or other artifice, the human population may increase to double in less than twenty years, unless wise deliberation supervenes. That is now the outline picture in Guiana, a multiplication which should cause a greater alarm than so far it does.[1] On the other hand the manatees begin to breed at an unknown age—perhaps six or seven at a guess—and can produce a calf at unknown intervals for an unknown number of years. Their fundamental breeding rate may indeed not be very different from that of men. But, and here is the vital difference, manatees still must sustain the pressures of a primitive mortality. And not only that, they must strive to sustain in addition the killing pressure of the human predators now rapidly escaping from their primitive mortality. Such is the burden of the manatee today. The life expectation constantly diminishes. The Guianan homeland may soon, by the loss of one more species—this time the manatee—be left by that much a less interesting place.

The problems of conservation are everywhere difficult, for the factors involved are many. The uneducated fun of the few integrates to become biological evil in the wider perspective of rationality. So biological conservation has come to be a matter of political judgement or, more frequently, neglect. However it would be unreasonable and probably unsuitable here to throw the mermaids into the British Guianan political scene and expect that they would swim. What however may be

1 See Appendix II.

reasonable is to attempt a picture of the wider Guianan scene, with special stress upon the biological, which includes the human, features and then again ponder the manatees as an aspect of the wider conservation picture.

Any worth-while assessment of conservational prospects anywhere must take account of the political stage of development of the relevant territory and the nature and diversity of its people. An assessment must be made of the present and likely influence and numbers of the cognoscenti, the biologically educated, and more particularly of those of them who have both enthusiasm and influence. Their number is nearly always very small. There must be consideration of the whole climate of interest and of opinion, of the standards of literacy and of education, of readiness for biological discipline and good sense. Often, reasonable theoretical prospects for conservation are clouded by a local excess of political disputation, litigiousness and the small-town atmosphere of personal criticism and parochialism. Important, too, for those who would prophesy and assess, is the relationship between human numbers and area, both countrywide and in particular regions.

It may be reasonably asserted that sound conservational practices, which regulate to best advantage the harvesting and perpetuation of the local fauna and flora, are an aspect of civilization in its widest sense. The furtherance of sound conservational practices demonstrates a wisdom that can contain the day after tomorrow, in a world where even the morrow is neglected by the many both in their public and in their personal lives and actions. The conservators of forests and mammals, of birds and fishes, of soil and water, are civilized beings with appreciation that the well-being of the children of men demands care of the human environment now. Little will it profit a family in the future if its dwelling is by this generation stripped of its finer furnishings. Care now is essential if the future is to have its fill of worth. It is axiomatic, too, that the greater the population density of our own species now, and the greater the expectation of large further increases, the greater must be the effort in biological conservation immediately. But the conservator is not alone in thinking of tomorrow and the day after tomorrow. That too is the duty, indeed the interest, of statesmen if not of a proportion of the personal-power-seeking politicians. The statesmen and the better politicians are seeking and working for improved conditions for their fellow human beings not just now but in the distant future too. These improved conditions often are largely pictured in terms of, truly, excessive material affluence. But the best of statesmen are thinking more in terms of improved human opportunities, of improved relationships between groups, of the denial of frustration and of the path of peace.

Conservators and statesmen ought, by their interests, to be in altruistic league together for the future well-being of that section of their own species for which they are temporarily responsible. Both have ideals, both a goal which is superior to that which exists today. Yet often conservator and statesman seem to be in foolish conflict, the one failing to recognize the worth and zeal of the other. Both in fact are striving, within their areas of special knowledge, whether environmental or relational, to promote the actual well-being of humankind. Their need is to agree on a goal, generalized though of necessity it would be, and subject as it would be, too, to all the imperfections of any highest common factor in a vastly complicated setting. An attempt has been made elsewhere[1] to state some such goal in brief verbal terms. 'A highly important part

1 *Adam's Brood* by Colin Bertram, p. 186. Peter Davies Ltd., 1958.

of any objective in life is to help to arrange that every person shall be born a loved and wanted child, with a good biological inheritance, and that each shall have the opportunity to develop to the full all the capacities with which he is endowed, physical, mental, and spiritual, in the service of his fellows. Such a definition intrinsically requires that the environment, our only home, shall be cherished—for, without that, full personal opportunity is impossible. That cherishing requires an extension of goodwill and love between ourselves to a neigh-bourliness towards the animals, and the plants too, which support us and give us joy.' Both the conservator and the statesman should find such a broad goal acceptable: neither should despise the contribution of the other.

The conservator, biologically educated, recognizes the need to maintain the quality of the living and productive environment within which future generations must live. He recognizes too that there may come a time, and that quite soon in some areas, when 'house full' is the truth—if reasonably desirable standards are not drastically to fall.

The statesman may perhaps be apt to imagine that the living environment is ever-stable and ever-productive, which certainly it is not. The statesman perhaps tends to focus his attention upon the social environment, the organization and the relationships between men, the opportunities for their social development, their education and their happiness. The conservator and the statesmen truly should be at one since both are seeking the long-term satisfaction of men's needs and their personal well-being in an earthly dwelling well furnished by providence and evolution. Only damnable are politicians who seek personal power and are too ignorant and self-assertive to become civilized statesmen.

Difference of opinions between conservators and statesmen expectedly may spring from limited views of the validity of the others' primary interests. Each must recognize the partial nature of his own expertise. Each works within a framework of time and trends. Both recognize the immense importance of education. It is sad that too often each is too busy to appreciate the other.

With such considerations in mind it may be reasonable to ponder a variety of aspects of the Guianan scene, yet most certainly not entering into the detail of personalities nor of political prospects. Much there is which all must face, all must live with, whether as leaders or as more humble individuals in an ever-changing world. These diverse aspects are all a part of reality, though their sum is not the whole of it. But another writer, in his different yet again individual way, would with equally good justification stress other aspects of the same reality. All are parts of the puzzle which must be fitted expeditiously if there is to be real progress towards any agreed and worthy aim or goal—and these two are one in fact for everlastingly as progress comes the aim should point to further goals.

So many of the leaders everywhere today are not statesmen but politicians only, mere dancers flitting across the vast floors of reality, even dancers upon a single table-top, dancers full of vigour and agility yet divorced from so large a part of reality. The fact that other dancers seek contemporaneously to dance upon the same small table indubitably makes them whirl the faster—until they fall—but brings much of reality no nearer. It has often been stated that in advanced democracies it is the period in opposition which alone allows the politician time to think anew, to descend from the table to the floor, to travel, to observe more widely, to compare and to gain further personal education in the perspective of the power which he has, as he hopes only temporarily, relinquished. So may he graduate to statesmanship, and the truth that politics is the art of the possible. Yet in the emergent nations of today the young leaders commonly assume or grasp responsibility and then cling to predominance in a way which denies them much of their own further potential growth in real stature. Perhaps unavoidable, this separation from the earth yet remains undesirable. Nevertheless, critical as we may sometimes appear to be of some among the emergent politicians, it is immensely to their credit that nearly all of them set education in the forefront of their policies. They do that to an extent which is admirably sensible in comparison with the priorities of the armament-minded leaders in some other lands.

The greatest danger to the second rate among the youthful politicians, everywhere today, is their spurious omniscience, a disease which afflicts far too many in every land on earth. But the larger the educated public the less is the danger. To attribute this disease exclusively to politicians would be wrong, for everywhere there are some afflicted—more frequently male than female—not by any means excluding the professional classes in the United Kingdom. Here we are in quandary. Dislike as we do that part of the character of those afflicted by fancied omniscience we have to recognize that it is, in large degree, this very spurious attribute itself which enables them to lead. Perhaps it is our own fault that in all walks of life, from politics to bingo, it is the fanatics who set the pace.

In our present context of interest in environmental conservation, usefulness and biological development, the danger lies in the felt omniscience of those politicians who are unmindful, inappreciative, of that wider reality which far exceeds the bounds of their own speciality—which is so ephemeral in time as well as space.

Whether we like it or not we cannot escape the fact that in almost every part of the globe today, a great measure of present physical and biological reality is the work of past men's hands. One may still travel in Antarctica, hundreds, even thousands of miles, in an environment still unsullied, unaltered, unimproved by man in both these senses. But over most of the globe today this is far from true. Few forests now are truly virgin, neither fired nor exploited by man; few stocks of birds and mammals have escaped the pressure of man's co-presence; few stocks of fishes exploitable by present techniques have still escaped exploitation and almost invariably severe depletion. Few areas have still seen nothing of man's present population surge, with its accompaniment of agriculture, road building, water management and town building. We view the products of change almost wherever we may go, but we usually forget that we are in fact viewing change—almost universally the work of past men's hands or the tokens of their presence.

Often those who have travelled the world and admired the works of men's hands must feel, on brief acquaintanceship, that the Guianas are singularly lacking in such material products of the past. There are no ancient walls, cathedrals, towers nor temples; no palaces, no great houses; no new buildings in concrete, glass and steel of notable proportions. Big bridges, substantial docks, railways, aqueducts, all are absent, though now the Affobakka dam[1] grows fast. Yet those who are more discerning will appreciate one special feature. The three Guianas together now total still under one million people despite their present world record rapid increase. Yet the labour of much smaller numbers over three and a half centuries have converted a tropical swamp coastline 500 miles long into a fertile seaboard of intensive agriculture. The outstanding

1 The Affobakka dam for the provision of hydroelectric power is the central feature of the Suralco Project in which the Government of Surinam and the Aluminum Company of America are in partnership.

effort has been the raising of continuous banks which keep out the sea from land whose natural level was little above half tide. The seaward walls of the earliest Dutch-planned polders are now practically continuous from one great river to the next. The cut waterways, distributaries and drains, channels and canals, in aggregate total thousands of miles. Mud and mangroves have changed to rice and sugar. The trees of the forest have been sawn, with early immense and latterly decreasing labour, to build a multitude of structures. From the cathedrals of Georgetown and Paramaribo, from the Palace of the Governor of Surinam, through the white painted and pleasing houses of the capitals to the humblest of huts, almost all is in wood. [1] The chief exceptions are some early buildings of Paramaribo, so attractive in their façades of imported red Dutch brick, the modern commercial buildings of the capitals in concrete, and the structures connected with the mining of bauxite. Notable, too, anywhere, would be the shining aluminium-clad Demerara sugar terminal whose bowels can store forty thousand tons of transit sugar at one time.

Banks and waterways, whatever their total length and the effort that went into their construction, are nevertheless unobtrusive. The many may live their lives without conscious recognition of the constructive handiwork of their forbears. Perhaps this seeming absence of material background, together with the psychological residuum of an earlier servitude, fosters in the people of the Guianas a restlessness, a lack of continuity, which now expresses itself in an eager forwardness which may prove in fact excessive.

Even the people, of any land of today, are of course in large

[1] Fascinating is the way in which in Surinam, even in the humblest and most elderly of little wooden shacks, the Dutch influence survives in the gable shapes, even hammered into corrugated iron and now totally non-functional.

degree the products of the activities of their forbears—not only through biological, reproductive activity of course. The people of today are the products for example of the maritime propensities of people in the past, people who voyaged and discovered, explored and exploited, who transported others in their thousands for profit whether under physical pressures or no. Whatever the motives, whatever the good or the ill involved, the people of today are the products of past peoples' activities, in war and in peace, and from that there is no escape. The people of today in the Guianas are—through the diverse activities and origins of their forbears and predecessors—a diversity of peoples, a mixture of those who differ still, rather than an amalgam or an ethnic compound. This inevitably has great influence on the political loyalties and prospects of today.

In the opposite sense, among the works of present men's forbears, much of the best timber of the Guianas has already gone, cut faster than it can grow and regenerate. Many of the mammals, the manatees among them, are greatly reduced in numbers; and of the larger, more elegant, more colourful, more easily shootable birds, now far fewer remain. Much has been burnt. Has this proved advantageous to the people of today? Has this been a necessary or an inevitable aspect of 'development' so that the people of today may lead richer lives? The rhetorical question should ever be a mode of stimulating thought.

What—a Martian might ask—is this 'development' of which so many talk so much? A large proportion of those many, if articulate or thoughtful enough to answer at all, will equate 'development' with an access of material objects and transformations. Those more thinking will give attention, too, to personal happiness and the sense of fulfilment. Without an access of those of what value is an access of material wealth?

The wise will have regard to the kinds of objectives which have been defined already, and will count 'development' as successive and successful steps towards agreed goals. They will recognize the importance of adequate nourishment, of increased expectation of life, of diminution of pain, anxiety and fear, and the control of frustration. So-called heightened standards of living in the sense of housing, transport and education will be included.

Much must go well for rapid development that is worthy. Among the requirements are hard work, together with the availability of enterprise and of finance. There must be a general acceptance of the direction of the development both in purpose and administratively. There must be a limitation of excessive material expectations too early and this must often include a self-denial of, truly, silly imports. There must be local peace and co-operation. To achieve much swiftly, and yet lastingly, there will probably be a seeking after financial aid and expertise from afar. There will be an avoidance of plain parasitism—upon those more affluent whether through special skills and hard work or fortuitous richness of natural resources —an avoidance of parasitism made possible by political intrigue and manufactured competition between great powers. There needs, too, to be realization that development takes time quite inevitably and that many others seek the same objectives contemporaneously.

For successful, happy development there needs to be more widespread recognition of two further aspects. The one is that, in general, higher standards require more work, at least for a period. Higher standards materially do not automatically produce higher levels of personal happiness. Some might really prefer and be happier with a humble material standard, considerable leisure—especially in hot climates—and moderate work. But such a state is unlikely to be chosen consciously by the people concerned whatever its truth in hindsight. The other aspect of development and the raising of material standards of the individual, is that in effect the individual requires and demands more personal space. That means not only more space for life and leisure but, additionally, more space to provide for each person his food and other new wants. A concomitant of increasing affluence is always a higher protein diet by choice and that inevitably takes more land for its production. More timber, textiles and tobacco for the individual likewise are reflected in a greater requirement of space per head.

These remarks touch upon just a few of the bare bones upon which the flesh of development may grow. It becomes a very difficult task indeed when, within any land, there are dissensions between people of differing racial origins, differing political affiliations and differing present standards already acquired; when there is a universal demand for material development at high speed yet in the absence of the experience of high taxation; and even more so when there is at the same time an actual population increase at a rate higher than almost anywhere else on earth.

Jeremiah died some years ago. He was, one supposes, a realist. He would perhaps have had some apt remarks about the developmental prospects of various places on earth today having regard to the incidence and the rate of change of the factors operating. Some factors are helpful to local development—determination, expertise, unity, and low cost production of commodities for the world market. Some factors are however unhelpful to development—disunity and too rapid present population increase being the most serious of them all. Where there is an excessive rate of present population increase, too much energy for development has to be diverted into stultifying efforts to maintain the *status quo* in education,

food, sufficiency and the rest. This last is a hard factual
lesson being now slowly learnt in many parts of the world.

In an Appendix (II) at the end of this book may come discussion of actual population increase in the Guianas, its cause,
excessive speed and result in the realms of education and employment—or rather unemployment. But here there may be
brief mention of another yet connected influence. Where
population increase is very rapid there do young people form
their largest proportion of the whole. Especially is this so in
lands such as the Guianas where special rapidity of increase
has come so suddenly and so recently. Half the total population
may be under the age of twenty. In such lands is group-
ebullience and youthful volatility at a maximum: in such lands
will the acceptable politicians be most youthful, perhaps more
full of zeal than wisdom and experience: in such lands may
revolution seem · more sensible than calmer evolutionary
advance in political affairs: in such lands—especially where
there are differential reproductive rates between those of
different racial, political or religious affiliations—may a
lowering of the age of voting to eighteen seem sensible, as
well as expedient to a party.

It is in lands where the average age is high that political
stability is most probable, yet where youth may become
politically apathetic, where the undergraduate may enquire
about his pension rights, where peace seems more important
than progress. It is a hypothesis which has much to recommend
it that fanaticism, whether of the left or of the right, most easily
takes root where unemployment is high and urban youth is
proportionately most abundant. It was in recognition of one
of the psychological facts of life that Dr Jowett on a notable
collegiate occasion remarked 'None of us is infallible—not
even the youngest among us.'

The buoyancy of seething youth may be educated, or lack

that opportunity, according to the chance of local circumstances. That buoyancy may, likewise, be led aright or astray, according to the chance availability of leaders of varied quality and judgement, and according to the stage in the political evolution of their homeland. It is so very understandable that at first sight, to youth, political change, social and material advancement, all seem so vastly more exciting and important than the checking of biological despoliation. What is around one seems so 'natural' in youth: there is no personal knowledge of what has been or of what might have been. Deforestation, over-grazing, and despoliation of savanna by fire, the loss of species, the decrease of gay birds and exciting beasts, all these mean nothing to youth, and more particularly urban youth. Education and knowledge, experience and travel, these are the ingredients which produce the conservators who worry and struggle, who care for plants, animals and living communities worldwide. It is the conservators who are the guardians of that biological grace without which humanity must live at a lower level of joy in the environment around us. Indeed lacking that grace man gradually and inevitably becomes self-destroying, spiritually and materially together.

Those who are conservators at heart—which means no more than rational in outlook and working for one's grandchildren as well as for oneself—conservators feel much frustration from the biological short-sightedness and greed of so many of their fellows everywhere. Conservation, as an outlook upon life and activity, is yet too civilized a spirit to be shared by the masses. It is the inherent optimism of those who would conserve which alone allows them to bear the frustrations of a world which contains so much that is biologically evil quite apart from the manifold evils of other varieties which beset us. It needs much optimism and desperate efforts to foster conservation when on almost every hand one sees the future fouled by every form of biological ignorance and thoughtlessness today. Must every small emergent nation of today allow its own despoliation rather than act upon the lessons so painfully learnt by more advanced nations through their own past folly? The United States has been alike the leader in past exploitational folly and in modern conservational practice. She has by no means rid herself of all irrational exploitational evil, but she certainly now nobly surpasses all others in new efforts at conservation of soil and living natural resources, forests, fisheries, mammals, birds. And the advantage is to the inhabitants, not to others at a distance.

To speak for the last time here of despoliation, take the dry savannas of the interior of Guiana, and the problem there of fire—fires which diminish or destroy the grazing and so desperately hinder attempts to raise the cattle productivity of the area.

Even seemingly civilized adults, we know, must play with fire, lighting an excessive number of matches so as to burn tobacco in pipes, and puff lung-cancer-stimulating cigarettes. So they take their drug and perhaps satisfy their primitive fire-playing instincts at the same time. So blame, in a sense, should not be too heavily cast upon those Amerindian children, and their elders too it is said, who love a blaze and to that end light matches from the box and cast the little flames by the wayside as they walk. A few square yards, an acre or two, or some square miles of fire soon follow and that surely is fun to see with any childish eyes—even if they are in a supposedly adult head.

It is true that firing of bush or savanna in Africa on occasion has its uses, and that pasture improvement may sometimes be obtained thereby. But such burning, if proved useful, must be on a basis of strict control and at considerable intervals of time. On the savannas of Guiana there is just no detailed knowledge, and certainly no evidence whatsoever that widespread and frequent firing is anything but inimical to pastoral productivity. Yet such firing continues and from all accounts increases in incidence year by year.

Here is an evil which increases in proportion to the availability of matches—an indication of a desirable rise in the standard of living it might otherwise be judged—and in proportion to the rise in population of the afflicted area. As elsewhere in Guiana, now even among the Amerindians the rate of population increase is high: the swelling of the school population is sufficient evidence of that. So an evil which is already great will progressively become much greater still to the detriment of the whole area.

The power to control is essential and that means the power to punish the offenders. Even more basic is the need for firm governmental decision that such burning is both harmful and must stop, because it hinders the cattle-producing potentiality of the homeland. Doubtless, as with ranching itself—whether in fact stagnant or progressive it is not for a zoological visitor to remark—there is a close connection with the systems of land tenure in force. Active ranchers, secure in a tenure which stimulated them to care for land improvement, would surely associate themselves and urge most strongly upon any government the abolition of savanna firing except under stringent control. This is one of those many matters of biological rationality which are intrinsically apolitical, and whose neglect condemns a government in the eyes of civilized people throughout the world.

The same logic is applicable to wild life destruction everywhere in the Guianas. The availability of firearms is in a sense a measure of a raised standard of living—just as is the availability of alcohol. Both need strict control for any nation's good. As the availability increases so does the population which may own, so that the total of firearms increases year by year astonishingly.[1] People shoot at all that moves, letting free alone the vultures. So game has gone, birds become scarce, the savannas blackened with fire to speed the process. The game-meat vanishes instead of being constantly available at rational harvest level. A government must take steps to control and punish, to restrict a spurious and foolish freedom to kill, to the end that posterity may possess a useful food-giving fauna, and the land remain furnished instead of becoming progressively more bare.

Certainly it must be recognized, and that with genuine sympathy, that politicians now are so heavily burdened with day to day short-term requirements—and a plethora of words seeming inescapable—that they fail to find the time for the longer-term apolitical biological problems of their homelands. Would that, like a judiciary immunized and isolated from politics, Biological Commissioners could be instituted for the control and rational exploitation of living natural resources in the public interest. To work to such an end, to employ such means, would set one country far above all others in the eyes of biologically civilized individuals throughout the world. Our manatee mermaids are obviously without political interests and political influence of their own, but their future existence depends fundamentally upon the possibility of wisdom in the politicians of today.

So we must leave the mermaids in the mud of Guiana, not at

1 There is a licensing system in B.G. for all firearms, but the licence fee is waived for Amerindians who now destroy at will over most of the country. More far-sighted, it is said, is the government of Venezuela which allows a single gun to each Amerindian village. That lethal instrument is sufficient to take an adequacy of wildlife so long as population increase is not excessive.

all even knowing their total number[1]—only that we believe they become much fewer and certainly they are less often to be seen. They are not yet truly to be described as rare animals but nowhere now can they be said to be abundant. Their number in Guiana cannot properly be assessed even as an order of magnitude except by guesswork. It may fairly be supposed that there are still in B.G. more than a thousand, but whether the real total exceeds that number by a factor of ten no one yet can properly assert, though we all may hope. Their future indubitably is problematical in these days of human demographic surge and efflorescence.

[1] As an example from afar, it is believed that there now are left no more than 14,000 rhinoceros in the whole of the continent of Africa.

Appendixes

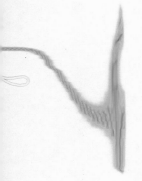

APPENDIX I

Manatee Legislation etc.

WESTERMANN[1] WRITING in 1953 gives a good general account of nature preservation in the Caribbean region, including the three Guianas. In those territories there has been little advance in the last decade with the exception of the B.G. manatee legislation of 1961 (see below).

With further reference to B.G., useful paragraphs may be quoted from an editorial article in the journal[2] of the Fauna Preservation Society in 1958.

'No resident mammal or bird of British Guiana . . . is known to have become extinct during the last 2,000 years. This has been due to the extensive forests and the small human populations of the past, but these factors cannot be relied upon indefinitely. The time to preserve animals and plants is before the threat to their existence has developed strongly.'

'British Guiana contains a great variety of interesting wild life typical of the Amazon basin. Among the abundance of mammals are the capybara, the largest existing rodent; the kinkajou; three species of anteater; the giant armadillo; the jaguar; the Brazilian tapir; howler, capuchin and spider monkeys; agouties and several species of deer. Amongst a wealth of birds are the extremely interesting and primitive hoatzin; the boatbill, the rosy flamingo and the rare harpy eagle.'

'Mammals receive complete protection in the Kaieteur National Park, an area of only forty-five square miles in the 83,000 square miles of British Guiana.'

1 See bibliography in Appendix III.
2 See pages 332–3 of *Oryx*, the Journal of the Fauna Preservation Society, Vol. IV, No. 5, London. 1958.

'Some birds receive nominal protection under the Wild Birds Protection Ordinance, which originated in 1919 but is admittedly ineffective. The Government has not put into effect the recommendations of successive committees on wild life protection. In September 1957 the following reply was given to a question on legislation for the protection of wild life put to the Minister for National Resources by Mr A. G. Tasker, O.B.E., a nominated member of Council: "The primary concern of the Government is the vigorous economic development of the country. Consequently, measures to promote such development will be given priority over the measures for which the need has not been definitely established." '

'There seems little indication that the Government of British Guiana intends to preserve the indigenous wild life of the country or the migratory birds which winter there.'

Yet every credit must be given to Mr Vincent Roth, until recently the Director of the Museum in Georgetown, and his active associates, for their efforts over the years to improve the situation and persuade Government to face its biological responsibilities.

Since 1958 in B.G. special efforts have been made by the Fisheries Department to introduce legislation for a close season for Arapaima, more especially in the face of commercial poaching from Brazil. So far there has been no success in this admirable effort.

However, legislation designed to protect the manatees has now successfully been passed into law—no mean achievement. Time will show how effective this legislation may prove to be in practise. Certainly as yet it is by no means fully protective since almost all are ignorant of its existence.

BRITISH GUIANA   No. 13 of 1961

REGULATIONS

Made under
The FISHERIES ORDINANCE, 1956
(No. 30 of 1956)

UNDER SECTION 33 OF THE FISHERIES ORDINANCE,
1956, THE FOLLOWING REGULATIONS HAVE BEEN
MADE BY THE GOVERNOR IN COUNCIL:

1. These Regulations may be cited as the Fisheries (Manatee Control) Regulations, 1961. *Short title.*

2. In these Regulations— *Interpretation.*
'food inspector' means a person entitled under section 18 of the Sale of Food and Drugs Ordinance to procure samples of food;
'water of the colony' includes any river, creek, reservoir, trench, lake or pond in the colony.

3. (1) It shall be lawful for a fishery officer to issue a licence to any person to capture, collect, remove or slaughter manatees found in any waters of the colony in such numbers and subject to such conditions as shall be set out in the licence. *Licence to capture etc. manatees.*

(2) There shall be charged a fee of five dollars in respect of each licence issued in accordance with these Regulations:

Provided that no fee shall be charged for the issue of a licence to capture, collect or remove any manatee which is at the time of the issue of such licence the subject matter of private ownership.

(3) A fishery officer shall be entitled in any case to refuse any application for the issue of a licence required by this regulation, subject to a right of review of the fishery officer's decision by the Director, whose decision shall be final.

(4) No person shall in any manner capture, collect, remove or slaughter any manatee whatsoever except in accordance with a licence issued under these Regulations.

4. Any person, not being a person licenced in accordance with these Regulations, who accidentally captures or kills any manatee shall immediately make a report to the Fisheries Division of the Department of Agriculture or to the nearest police station.

Accidental capture or killing of manatee.

5. (1) Every manatee that dies or is killed shall be examined by a food inspector and an officer of either the Fisheries Division or the Veterinary Division of the Department of Agriculture before any portion of the meat thereof is disposed of or used for human consumption.

Inspection of carcase of manatee.

(2) A food inspector who examines the carcase of a manatee shall, where he so finds, issue a certificate that the meat thereof is fit for human consumption; otherwise the food inspector shall order that the carcase be destroyed.

(3) No person shall expose for sale, sell or otherwise dispose of the meat of any manatee intended for human consumption unless such meat has been examined and certified in accordance with paragraphs (1) and (2) of this regulation.

(4) Any person found in possession of the carcase or any meat of a manatee which has not been examined and certified in accordance with paragraphs (1) and (2) of this regulation shall be guilty of an offence under these Regulations.

6. Subject to the provisions of regulation 3 of these Regulations, nothing in these Regulations shall prevent any person from acquiring and exercising rights of ownership over any manatee.

Private ownership.

7. Any person who injures, molests or does any act of cruelty to any manatee whatsoever shall be guilty of an offence under these Regulations.

Cruelty to manatee.

8. Any person found in possession of a manatee or the carcase of a manatee in respect of which there has not been either—

Unlawful possession of manatee.

   (a) a licence issued for its capture, collection, removal or slaughter in accordance with these Regulations; or

   (b) a report made in accordance with these Regulations that it has been accidentally captured or killed,

shall be guilty of an offence under these Regulations.

9 In any prosecution for an offence under these Regulations the onus of proving that—

Onus of proof.

   (a) a manatee has been captured or killed accidentally:

   (b) a manatee has been captured, removed, collected or slaughtered under a licence issued in accordance with these Regulations.

   (c) a manatee or the carcase of a manatee is the subject matter or private ownership;

   (d) a manatee or the carcase or meat of a manatee has been examined by a food inspector and certified as fit for human consumption,

shall rest upon the person charged with the offence.

10. Any person who commits a breach of these Regulations shall be liable on summary conviction to a fine not exceeding fifty dollars or to imprisonment for a term not exceeding two months and to forfeiture of any licence issued to him under these Regulations.

Offence.

Made in Council this 25th day of July, 1961.

A. A. ABRAHAM.
Clerk to the Executive Council.

(M. P. AGR.2/15/6).

APPENDIX II

The Human Problem
of the Guianas

BRITISH GUIANA remains in travail, attempting to achieve an Independence which is seemingly much desired in the hearts and minds of a large proportion of the inhabitants: early Independence is regarded as a desirable objective in Whitehall too. Yet the London Conference in October and November 1962 ended without agreement between the Guianese factions and their leaders. Their views on procedure differed strongly in addition to their views on the new constitutional framework itself. That, in general, the assembled leaders seemed to represent differing interests and differing ethnic groups will be remarked by many. The passage of time may yet force compromises previously thought to be impossible. On the other hand new events may lead to struggles yet unforeseen. The troubles[1] of February 1962 in Georgetown showed how easily the peaceful assembly of those with a common grievance may switch to turmoil. Rapid increase of both population and under-employment are indeed regular precursors of trouble the world over.

A population picture of the Guianas may now be given[2] because it is intrinsically of great interest; because it is in fact the overwhelming influence in Guianan affairs; and because the background demographic movements of human beings provide the environment in which other species of animals—like manatees—will sink unaided but may swim to usefulness if helped. The human demographic

1 Report of a Commission of Inquiry into Disturbances in British Guiana in February 1962. H.M.S.O. London. Colonial No. 354.

2 The following paragraphs are an extended version of the theme of the author's short paper in the *Eugenics Review*, Vol. 54.2. July 1962: 'A Population Picture of British Guiana'.

surge, and all its tremendous problems, must not so daunt the politicians that all other species must suffer and die through overlaying. The leaders and politicians need all the help that can be given by people of goodwill and biological sense everywhere to help them gain the perspective required to surmount the local difficulties. But the task will be troublesome and prolonged, and vestigial evaluations of human life must be uprooted. The mere existence of human life in bulk must cease to seem sufficient, being supplanted by recognition of the quality and liberty of life for all as individuals. Here then is the picture.

One of the placards carried in the peaceful processions through Georgetown, B.G., on the day before the riots of 16 February 1962, carried the slogan 'The Budget means Birth Control'. The next one, in a different vein, said 'Capitalists are no Angels but we still need Them'. Muddled thinking and mixed motives were very evident in this land now so sadly reft by racial tensions between those of African and those of peninsular Indian origin, after a peaceful co-existence of over a hundred years.

It is not the political background in B.G. that needs comment here though its ramifications and influence are quite inescapable. The fundamental recognition is needed that the Guianas, and indeed almost the whole Caribbean area, form a region both of great demographic interest and one which offers immense scope for humanitarian effort on a most intensive scale.

World population increase is now at a rate of about 1·7 per cent per year which will result in doubling by the end of the century, from about three thousand millions today to about six thousand millions then. So far, all reputable prophecies of future world numbers are being overtaken by events. B.G., now at 600,000, itself is doubling in under twenty years with a rate of increase of 3·43 per cent per year[1], almost the very highest in the whole world. This prodigious and frightening population increase was never

1 See '1960 Demographic Yearbook', issued by the Statistical Office of the United Nations. The British Guiana rate of population increase is only exceeded by (American) Samoa 3·45; Grenada 3·46; St Vincent 3·52; Cook Islands 3·56; British Honduras 3·67; Surinam (Dutch Guiana) 3·77; and Brunei 4·5.

sought, has no evident positive advantages, and is a totally unplanned by-product of the long beneficent effort which culminated
in the local conquest of malaria. The sequence and the figures are
well known. Up until the end of World War II mortality from
malaria, especially in infancy, was extremely high. By that time Dr
Giglioli, the eminent malariologist, had unravelled the background
entomology and the relative importance of the local anopheline
mosquitoes. *Anopheles darlingi* was the culprit, an intensely
anthropophilic species, always seeking man and his dwellings.
Immediately upon the coming into wide availability of DDT
in 1945 and 1946, an intensive campaign was instituted of
spraying the inside walls of all places of human habitation in the
entire coastal strip of British Guiana. The results were spectacular.
Within a few years *Anopheles darlingi* was virtually extinct; new
cases of malaria simply did not occur; infantile mortality fell pro-
digiously; and the population embarked upon its unprecedented
upward leap. The local population surge was indeed an unplanned
by-product of the proper beneficent effort to rid the people of a
crippling load of malaria. The results are remarkable both for good
and for ill.

Whatever the outside view may be, the internal opinion on the
demographic position is the one that, naturally, is reflected in local
policy. In this field there is indeed wide divergence at present
between the two. Reminding ourselves that the limitation of con-
ception[1] has two primary reasons, the one personal and humanitarian, the other demographic and economic, let us view the
scene.

At present there is seemingly complete local belief that 'development'[2] will be sufficiently rapid to take care of the speeding population increase, indeed that such increase may even be valuable to
help forward 'development'. By Caribbean standards, B.G. is a

1 The work of the International Planned Parenthood Federation
and of national Family Planning Associations in so many lands.

2 It is both salutary and of interest to turn back to the wisdom
embodied in the Report of the West Indies Royal Commission of
1938–9 (Cmd. 6607. 1945). 'An awakening of public opinion is
indeed the indispensable condition of a solution of this problem' of
over-population, 'and every body and organization that seeks, in
whatever sphere, to guide or influence opinion should recognize

large country, some 83,000 square miles of the South American continent. A single island in the mouth of the Essequibo River exceeds in area the whole of Barbados which supports nearly a quarter of a million people, tight packed though they may be. The present population of British Guiana is confined to little more than coastal and riverine strips totalling perhaps two hundred miles long and about five miles wide. The remainder of the country is occupied by few other than some thousands of Amerindians. The 'development of the interior'—hydro-electric power, forestry, ranching, gold and diamonds[1]—is a goal which raises high hopes beyond the present reliance upon bauxite, sugar and rice. Potentiality may glitter, but feasibility is always open to debate when real attempts are made to appraise the situation. Further, the observer will probably conclude that whatever developments may come they will not be such as to demand large numbers of individual men and women for their advancement. Capital and vigour, expertise, machinery and

---

the responsibilities that rest upon it to assist and not to obstruct the process of public enlightenment' in the matter of contraception. When those words were written the rate of population increase which was regarded as dangerous was under 2 per cent per annum, while now B.G. has gone up to nearly 3½ per cent. Whatever the theoretical potentialities for development it is the actual rate of population increase which impedes progress in so many ways.

It may be of interest in this whole context to refer to the present author's 'Settlement Prospects in the West Indies: Review' in the *Geographical Journal*, Vol. CXII, Nos. 4–6. October–December 1948. pp. 219–24 which reviews and collates that series of notable documents and Reports on the West Indies which emerged between 1939 and 1948.

1 Hopes in diamonds in the Guianas are such that the following world figures may have interest. The annual world production of mined diamonds is 25 million carats which is the equivalent of five tons. These five tons consist of one ton of gem stones and four tons of abrasive diamond for industrial use. The 'value' of the gem stones is not properly assessable. The four tons of industrial diamonds have a value of about £20 million, and they come from the sorting of about 125 million tons of diamondiferous ore. From S. Tolansky. 'Technological Importance of Industrial Diamond'. *Nature*, No. 4826. 28/4/62, p. 341.

a few skilled men, would seem the real requirements. The outsider may think that the actual rate of the 'development of the interior' will by no means be commensurate with an accelerating rate of population increase already causing a doubling in under twenty years. The previous doubling in numbers took just forty years, which is about the present rate for the world as a whole.

On the other hand local opinion is totally different: there is faith that 'development' will absorb all the extra hands which the years will bring. There is faith that gifts and loan capital will flow in (or ought to flow in) from the outside world to speed such development. There is determination that mainland B.G. shall provide for its own and not for the overspill populations fast-multiplying in the Caribbean islands. Any suggestions that contraceptive measures are desirable on demographic and economic grounds at present find few listeners. Local belief of this kind, however, among leaders is inadequate to check an outward flow of individuals who, making decisions for themselves, seek opportunity elsewhere but especially in the United Kingdom. That over-crowded island has now been forced, sadly, to introduce immigration control where until recently there was none.[1]

In the realms of family planning, in terms personal and humanitarian, the position in B.G. is extraordinary and most saddening but so very ripe for progress. Political emotion and insinuation, racial tension and the desire for a maximum of voters, all aid the burying of heads in mud. No political leaders nor public figures will outspokenly demand or strive for a programme of birth control now, even on purely humanitarian grounds, to relieve a maternal misery and squalor which are appalling. Private discussion with potential leaders or activators of opinion demonstrate clearly the difficulties in which they find themselves. They are aware, but seemingly they cannot act even though they aver that substantial efforts in family planning would be acceptable almost everywhere. Opposition they regard as small and likely in any event to be ephemeral—if only somebody would do something, somebody not inhibited by local

1 The Commonwealth Immigration Act 1962. For some of the causes and considerations preceding the Act, see for example the author's 'West Indian Immigration', Occasional Paper Number One of the Eugenics Society. 1958.

political and other pressures. The Roman Catholic difficulty in B.G. is not large and experience elsewhere has demonstrated its wasting nature.

Contrasting, and somewhat simplifying the racial and other divergencies, by leaving aside other important but very much smaller groups, the urban people in B.G.[1] are mainly of African origin and Christian belief; they are fortunate in the possession of a markedly higher standard of living than is common in the whole Caribbean region. The rural people, in general of Hindu Indian origin, live much closer to the earth, and are mostly engaged in the cultivation of sugar or of rice. To the urban population, whose wants are now largely met by imported articles of every kind, contraceptives are available as from chemists shops in England. The ignorance of the majority, rather than lack of availability and opportunity, is there the obstacle. In the rural areas the standard of living is low by contrast with the capital, Georgetown, but less low than in many of the tropical areas of the world. Total ignorance of contraception, lack of availability and lack of facilities are, as elsewhere, the normal features of this mode of life.

The condition, in particular of rural Indian mothers, is now so often one of indescribable dejection and anxiety. The girl, pregnant at sixteen by arrangement in a marriage in which she is the female pawn, produces her near annual infant with a regularity which appals. Before 1945 a considerable proportion of the swarm was carried away by malaria in youth, a succession of small tragedies overcome by the pressure of successors. Now the great majority survive whether nourished sufficiently or less. The economic burden is heavy, the house is too small, the never well-tied husband frequently departs to women fresh and new, and the mother struggles on in penury and malnutrition. Seven or eight children by age

[1] The B.G. example is here stressed for the evidence is more clear cut and conflict has already arisen in much stronger form. But Surinam already has a still higher annual percentage rate of increase of population. In addition to those of African and those of peninsular Indian origin, Surinam also contains a comparable group of people of Javanese origin. All three groups are, in comparison with B.G., more integrated both in interests and in mode of life, appearing all three of them in both the urban and the rural scenes in more even proportions. That may help stability.

twenty-three is by no means rare, and a score of parturitions in apathetic misery is the lot of many. The multipara almost emulate those Palolo worms which meet death split asunder by the immensity of their reproductive effort. That is no emancipation of women, though—differing from their sisters in Switzerland and the Yemen—they have indeed the vote in a blind universal suffrage where race counts more than capacity or sense. These overburdened apathetic and miserable multipars are not conceivably capable of leading such an abundance of offspring towards good citizenship in a modern setting.

Perhaps such a description may be thought too dispiriting and blunt. But go to a hospital and look, both in the ward and in the book which records the ages of the girls and the number of their previous children. No sound nation can be built on such misuse of womanhood, on such profligacy of reproduction and such rapidity of overall increase. Never before has there been such large-scale profligacy in reproduction combined with so high a survival rate among those produced.[1]

The government rural hospital services are very importantly enlarged by the philanthropic efforts of the Bookers group of companies. This group has many activities among which its management of eighty per cent of the sugar estates of B.G. is notable. In this activity Bookers are substantial employers of labour, largely of cane cutters who are very subject to miscellaneous injuries and ills. Kindness has led now to an embarrassment, in the extension of care to the families of employees. And that means maternity work both in the provision of estate midwives, and in the hospitalization and after-care of worn-out girls. The propriety of contraceptive advice and facilities under these conditions would be debatable quite apart from the usual difficulties in the humble homes in which the women live and breed. It is noteworthy, but not novel, that the midwives are paid on the basis of actual deliveries. Their help with contraceptive advice would naturally be problematical. This is no novel circumstance in biological economics and it can be overcome.

The outside observer may note with interest the historical

1 The Mennonite community in the eastern United States has, however, managed to increase its numbers from 300 in 1874 to over 9,000 today, aided by agricultural and religious zeal.

evolution of social customs which has led to the wide acceptability now, in the villages of peninsular India, of voluntary sterilization of men with three or more children, in government clinics. Among people of like antecedents a few generations back but now living in Guiana, sterilization is so far a rare and special medical aid for weary women already with many children.

Turn now to the future. It must be admitted that in the world setting B.G.'s population and importance are not great. Its women, in particular the rural, suffer a misery which is avoidable only by the rapid growth of family planning facilities. However, if prophecy is to be made it is that in fact there will be no early amelioration of their present distress through local effort. Further, whatever nucleus there may be of potential local leaders in this area of sorely needed social service, those leaders are likely for some while to feel so restricted by special local impediments that mere monetary aid and encouragement from afar will be insufficient. This normal form of encouragement to indigenous effort may on occasion be inadequate. If the observer may be permitted a judgement, it is that, in the special local circumstances pertaining to B.G. the need is for outside aid in the form of clinics set up with outside money and outside staff, both provided by a philanthropic international organization or great foundation. That would be the yeast which might then in quite a short space of time activate local leadership and so leaven and transform the Guianan family pattern towards a personal happiness which is not possible for a multitude of women today. In the first instance the minimum local requirement might be an informal assurance from the Prime Minister that any internationally reputable clinic organization would receive no official obloquy. It is not too much to hope that such an assurance would become available.

It is evident to the outsider in any problem such as this, that the approach towards the essential gross demographic limitation will come only via the stimulus of humanitarian effort for the sake of individuals. Further discussion of this fundamental topic should be reserved for another place, but stress again is here essential that under modern conditions great contemporary percentage population increase is an adverse factor, a terrible impediment, to speedy local development. The Guianas might well take note of India's example—though her present efforts to reduce her percentage annual population increase, in the interests of her own development, may well prove to be inadequate, brave as they are.[1]

Turn now to the educational problem—the finding of teachers adequate in numbers and in quality. This is a sufficiently difficult problem in near stable populations like that of the United Kingdom when there is simply the desire to raise the school leaving age by another year, and increase the opportunity for higher education. The educational problem in any land of high population incremental rate is inevitably far greater still. It is great even in highly advanced countries like the United States where the annual population increase is about 1·75 per cent. It is much greater still in poor and under-developed small lands where population increase already exceeds 3 per cent per annum, and daunting indeed in the Guianas where B.G. grows at 3·43 per cent and Surinam at 3·77 per cent per year. The twin problems of physical premises and of staff must both be solved and of these the former is the easier to meet if the will and a little cash are there together. Shortage of money fortunately is offset in tropical lands by the simpler forms of construction which may be sufficient. But shortage of staff is all the more serious because training facilities locally are notable for their paucity. The profession of teaching, nowhere in a materialistic world, is held in high regard among the masses, and the stipends are small. The Guianas are not Scotland in the nineteenth century with a high indigenous regard for the teaching profession. At a time, too, of rapid increase in the school population, the form of the educational pyramid becomes of immediate conscious concern to many parents and children, ministers and masters alike, and to the generality of tax payers. Where funds, premises and teachers are all inadequate in quantity a fierce competition arises and priorities must be determined. Are the primary

1 In a House of Lords debate on 6 June 1962 Lord Casey quoted the Indian Ambassador to the United States as follows: 'There are three specific kinds of assistance of which India is desperately in need. The sharing of experiences in population control by the advanced countries; the very substantial increase in research in the United States for a simple and inexpensive contraception method; thirdly, technical aid, especially of manufacturing facilities for family planning supplies.' Indian minds are opening while those of Indians in Guiana seem so far to remain closed to demographic realities.

requirements of the masses to take precedence or the training of a
deliberately selected élite which may be influential in a technological
era? And what of special schools for children handicapped in mind or
body? Must they have no chance now so that those more fortunate
may develop to the limits of their much finer capacities? It is at such
times that the academics, the head masters and head mistresses of
education, strive and compete in their views upon the thorny content
of syllabi and curricula. In all these realms harsh compromises must
inevitably be made. Ministers of Education the world over would do
well to remember that the best teachers and academics have high
professional standards and will move elsewhere if pushed too hard.
Can the gaps—in the Guianas or elsewhere—be filled? Where in the
world is there a superfluity of graduates, a possible plethora of
potential teachers albeit at more humble levels? Are the stories true
of the many unemployed young Indian graduates, class III degrees
on their scrolls and their hands in their semi-westernized pockets,
seeking a white collar employment which peninsular India, to her
own detriment, cannot as yet provide or afford? The need and the
opportunity for compromise may be great whatever the unpredict-
able consequences which may ensue for both potential provider and
receiver.

Throughout the world high population increase is linked with
under-employment and unemployment. That so far is true of the
Guianas whatever may be the demand for skilled labour and
machinery minders where rapid physical development occurs. The
Suralco project, building the great dam at Affobakka in Surinam, is a
prime example. Technologically speaking, these are days demanding
trained brains, and brains linked with skilled hands, not unskilled
labour linked with brains unstretched. The export industries of B.G.
are sugar and bauxite, both of them, in their respective ranges and for
perfectly sound reasons, tending to be relatively high cost producers.
If those industries are to survive as taxable entities in a competitive
world, they must check and endeavour to reduce their costs of production. The one method, which they cannot possibly avoid is
progressive further mechanization. That tendency means two
things, the first the sinking of still further capital, the second the
reduction in the total requirement of labour.

In this last regard even our mermaids in their muddy channels
have been placed there experimentally to do jobs otherwise done

with human hands. If the manatee channel clearance experiments were to be entirely successful, and the creatures were to multiply and flourish, they would put out of employment an uncalculated number of men and women who, otherwise, cutlass in hand would toil in the heat, season by season, amid the mud and weed. And the alternative? Is it to sink more capital in machinery or weedicides, technological developments which again provoke unemployment?

When the need and the tendency are both towards the reduction of the total labour employed, it is unfortunate, to say the least, that contemporaneously there should be local increase in the ranks of the potentially employable at a rate almost unprecedented in world history. That way does not lead to local happiness.

It is again a world wide experience, and really very obvious, that unemployment and under-employment make for internal tensions and the seeking of scapegoats. Visible differences among the people of an area, divergencies of community interests and activities, all these realities assist and canalize whatever tensions may arise or be propagated. Thus a plural society, where integration of customs, interests and relative affluence are by no means complete, is most subject to tension and conflict. Unemployment and under-employment in the Guianas are doing just this, within a pattern now not rare. Unemployment deepens those fissions within the land between those whom fate has decreed shall be urban, of African origin and of one political inclination, as against for example those who are rural, of peninsular Indian origin and of another political pursuasion. The volatility of young populations and the dogmatism of politicians do not help to sooth the rifts which in such circumstances are inevitable. The extreme rate of population increase in its power to magnify unemployment is like the addition of a blow-lamp to the side of a kettle which is already boiling.

Yet democracy is built on the mutual assumption and trust that the party in power will not go beyond the rules and customs which are tacitly agreeable to majority and minority alike.

The historians record what happens in the realms of political agitation and ferment, physical violence and fire and riot. But few historians will, one fears and fancies, be biologically aware enough to follow through the sequence, a chain reaction, so fantastically stimulated by advances in medical knowledge and particularly the eradication of malaria from the Guianas' coastal plain in the middle nineteen-forties.

There are always some, of a more optimistic turn of mind, who regard unemployment as the opportunity for development, for great physical works which shall be of lasting benefit to the whole community. The building of roads, it will be argued, is a case in point where the labour of many may provide future dividends for the community as a whole. Likewise the building and strengthening of coastal walls and sea defences, and again the digging of canals to facilitate inland east-west transport, may be brought forward as most worthy schemes. The availability of the completed schemes most certainly would be advantageous: it is the steps towards them which may test capacity and indeed morality. All such types of public works in these days can in fact most cheaply, efficiently and quickly be carried out by heavy earth-moving machinery making use of small numbers of skilled operatives. The carrying of countless baskets of earth on the heads of countless women while their men shovelled and dug and spread and rolled was all very well when there was no alternative. It may still be so if the people concerned, otherwise unemployed, are sufficiently and totally ignorant of modern mechanisms and possibilities. But in fact of course they are not. Such great works can only now be carried out by hand power when the manual workers concerned are compelled either by a fanatical zeal or by an extraneous physical force, or by fear of some other type. None of these stimulators to immense activity are desirable, though a spiritual zeal, indigenous in origin, must certainly not be condemned. The kibbutzim of Israel in recent years have shown something of it. The whole problem is of the essence of dilemma. The development of the interior of the Guianas is not work for the unemployed of the coastal strip. Likewise, land development projects for the extension of the agricultural potential require machinery for their progress and then skilled and vigorous cultivators for their fulfilment. The common run of the unemployed are not ideal people for immediate settlement in the new area. There is experience enough of that the world over.

Casting around for alternatives when in seeming dilemma is always the most sensible of exercises. In the present content a rumour current in Cayenne, (French Guiana), may have relevance. There, in that Department of France which sends its Deputies to

Paris, army conscription it is said is soon to be introduced for the first time. The plan apparently is that the first six months shall be spent on military training. Thereafter eighteen months will be spent on public projects which can be termed 'development', roads in particular being on the programme. Yet there is need to bear in mind, when making estimates and judgements, just what are the relative demographic and geographical factors which are relevant. Very roughly speaking the three Guianas are—in order from east to west and referring to them by those older national adjectives which have now become pejorative—of comparable area and mainly forest-covered. The great majority of the inhabitants live on the narrow coastal strip which is almost absent in French Guiana and at its widest in western British Guiana. French Guiana totals 30,000 people of whom 17,000 are in Cayenne the capital. Dutch Guiana has 300,000 people of whom 115,000 are in Paramaribo the capital. British Guiana has near 600,000 people of whom 100,000 are in Georgetown the capital. Facts are needed before judgement and this is but a tiny selection of the needed facts. But the outsider may be excused wondering whether present fissiparous tendencies are not more emotional than wise. The central world tendency is for larger groupings while contemporaneously the peripheral areas still fragment. Might a Greater Guiana be to the advantage of all Guianese of whatever origin? The advantages might in fact be very considerable, each one supplementing the others mutually. The expectations for such an arrangement are however probably extremely slim: parochialism prospers in places long left in peace without real troubles on their borders.

Where, as is usual in tropic lands, there is inadequate local capital and expertise for development, then trust must be engendered to make easier its supply from afar. There was real sense in that slogan 'Capitalists are no Angels but we still need Them'. And all help comes most easily where the receiver is already helping himself to the limits of local capacity and where fanatics are not excessively in evidence. Extreme rapidity of population increase, as already stressed, in its stimulus to tension and fanaticism is a contra-indication in the provision of capital. The help becomes swallowed in excess.

Stability of population is not by any means necessary for real development. These are matters of degree. But very high rates of population increase most certainly are strongly inimical to those forms of development where the well-being of individuals is included among the aims. These are harsh facts of life—but they are facts. Likewise, too rapid population increase is the worst of bedfellows for that proper conservation of natural resources which is the main topic of this book.

In any situation of complexity, where there is zeal to approach worthy objectives, the need is for the sensible adjustment of all the variable factors. Among these in our present era progressively emerges population growth, that contemporary by-product of beneficence and knowledge. In large degree we now have the powers and the responsibilities of decreased mortality and extension of personal life, and we exercise those powers. Likewise today we have —or can have through education and the provision of facilities—in large measure the powers and the responsibilities for the making of human life. And we can do so at a rate which is sensible both economically and within the freedom of individuals. Those responsibilities must be exercised; and without some success in that, much which is desirable and for which we strive will not be attained. The checking of the excessive annual rates of increase is difficult but yet a reasonable prospect. Other lands throughout the world are facing boldly and contemporaneously the selfsame problems. Apart from straightforward humanity to the thousands of suffering women bowed down by repeated pregnancies and unwanted further children, there is every sensible incentive to the deliberate reduction of present rates of population growth. In such excessive growth there are no positive advantages[1] whatsoever and only a tangled web of new difficulties. The advance of education and of development, and the containment of growing unemployment, would all be fostered by diminished rates of increase. It is only the cynical who will point to the fact that unscrupulous politicians, religionists and others, may find temporary sectarian advantage in the multiplication of their own kind irrespective of poverty and dejection—so long as those produced shall have the vote.

[1] For a wider consideration of this topic see for example the present author's chapter 'What are People for?' in *The Humanist Frame*, a symposium volume edited by Julian Huxley. George Allen and Unwin, 1961.

APPENDIX III

Short Bibliography of Recent Books and Reports

Detailed references are shown in footnotes in the text.

ALLEN, Glover, M. *Extinct and vanishing Mammals of the Western Hemisphere with the Marine Species of all the Oceans.* 1942 Special Publication No. 11 of the American Committee for International Wild Life Protection. New York Zoological Park.

CAMACHO, R. F. General Review of Drainage and Irrigation in the Coastal Plain and Report for the years 1957, 1958 and 1959 on the Drainage and Irrigation Department.
1960. Published by Authority of His Excellency the Governor of British Guiana.

COLONIAL OFFICE. Reports on British Guiana. Her Majesty's Stationery Office, London.

DARLINGTON, P. J. *Zoogeography.* 1957. John Wiley and Sons, New York.

HAYMAN, R. W. *Manatees and Dugongs.*
1956. Zoo Life No. 10. London.

HOWELL, A. Brazier. *Aquatic Mammals: their adaptations to Life in the Water.*
1930. Charles C. Thomas, Springfield, Illinois.

MOHR, E. *Sirenen oder Seekühe.*
1957. Die Neue Brehm-Bücherei, A. Ziemsen Verlag. Wittenberg Lutherstadt.

ROTH, Vincent. *Notes and Observations on Animal Life in British Guiana.*
1941. The *Daily Chronicle* Ltd. Georgetown, British Guiana.

SMITH, Raymond T. *British Guiana.*
   1962. Oxford University Press. Issued under the auspices of the
   Royal Institute of International Affairs.
SWAN, Michael. *British Guiana. The Land of Six Peoples.*
   1957. Her Majesty's Stationery Office, London.
WESTERMANN, J. H. *Nature Preservation in the Caribbean.*
   1953. Publications of the Foundation for Scientific Research in
   Surinam and the Netherlands Antilles, Martinus Nijhoff, The
   Hague.